THE MAN ACROSS THE RIVER

RIVER

THE INCREDIBLE STORY OF ONE MAN'S WILL TO SURVIVE THE HOLOCAUST

ZVI WIESENFELD

ISBN: 9789493231078 (ebook)

ISBN: 9789493231061 (paperback)

Publisher: Amsterdam Publishers, The Netherlands

info@amsterdampublishers.com

CONTENTS

In memory of my grandfather, Jacob Wiesenfeld

Jacob was left alone on the far side of the river. A stranger appeared and wrestled with him until just before daybreak. When the stranger saw that he could not defeat Jacob, he touched the upper joint of Jacob's thigh. Jacob's hip joint became dislocated during the struggle.

"Let me go," said the stranger. "Dawn is breaking."

"I will not let you leave until you bless me."

"What is your name?"

"Jacob."

"Your name will no longer be Jacob, but Israel. You have grown strong before God and man. You have won."

(Genesis 32)

PREFACE

I was studying in Israel when my grandfather, Jacob Israel Wiesenfeld, passed away. I was 18 years old and enrolled in the post-high school program at the *Yeshivat Kerem B'Yavneh* Talmudic seminary, located on a *kibbutz* twelve kilometers east of the Mediterranean port town of Ashdod. I received the call from my father in my Spartan dorm room on Sunday morning, the first day of the Hebrew month of *Kislev,* November 10, 2007.

"Zvi, I just want to let you know that Saba passed away."

"Oh. *Baruch Dayan HaEmes*" (Blessed be the True Judge).

"Do you want to come home for the funeral?"

I didn't want my parents to spend the money. "No, I'm good."

"That's fine. Stay and *learn* (study) in his memory."

My grandfather had been ill for some time. He had spent his last few months at my parents' house in northern New Jersey. He was eventually admitted to Maimonides Hospital near his home in the Borough Park section of Brooklyn. There, my grandfather contracted a staph infection. The infection proved fatal.

The funeral was held the following day. I sat huddled around a Nokia cell phone in my cousin Dovi's cramped apartment in the Beis Yisroel neighborhood of Jerusalem. Dovi was studying in the Mirrer Yeshiva at the time. His mother, my aunt, called Dovi and muted her phone for the duration of the service. In this manner, my cousin and I listened to relatives eulogizing our grandfather.

Stories about my grandfather's hellish experiences in Europe were conspicuously absent from the eulogies. The Holocaust left him utterly traumatized; he never talked about it – not to anyone.

My grandfather was the kindest, gentlest man I ever met. He worked hard and was devoted to his family and community. He was one of my role models and had an outsized influence on my life. Yet, I didn't truly know him. Very few people really did. He hid his pain away.

Several years ago, my sister and I were discussing my grandfather and his astonishing life. "We are the last generation to personally know survivors," I said to her. "The Holocaust dies with us. Someone needs to find out what happened to Saba."

I decided to write a book.

I traced my grandfather's life from the Yiddish-speaking Jewish Quarter of Czernowitz to the killing fields of Transnistria and to the region's concentration camps. I learned about his time as a conscript in the Red Army, his status as a refugee in an Italian displaced persons' camp, his arrival on Ellis Island and his struggles as an immigrant in a new land.

This slim volume is the result of interviews with everyone I could find who knew my grandfather, gathering partially formed anecdotes and snippets of stories. I then deeply researched the Holocaust in Romania and the Ukraine until I was able to include the stories in a larger narrative. I filled in many details myself. I imagined virtually all of the dialogue and some of the characters. The result is a work of biographical fiction based upon the life story of a remarkable man. Throughout, I strove to do justice to my grandfather's story and to honor his memory.

MAPS

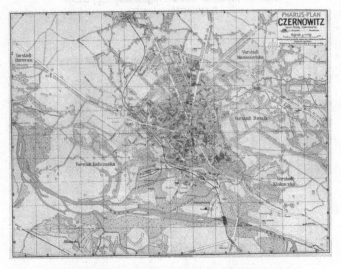

Map of Czernowitz by Leon Koenig. From: http://czernowitz.ehpes.
com/czernowitz3/newmaps/20sCzCity.jpg

Romanian Camps and Ghettoes, 1942. Collection: United States Holocaust Memorial Museum. https://images.app.goo.gl/ FeLYEBDH9mebpYB66

1

Dawn broke over Czernowitz as Yankel Wiesenfeld-Reiner hurried home, pulling his tattered coat tightly to him against the autumn chill of November 1937. It was a long shot, but there was a chance that he could get home and crawl into bed before Zushe awoke for morning *shacharis* prayers. He didn't think he had the energy for one of Zushe's lectures. Yankel tried to ignore the cold ache in his feet, protected only by thin stockings and a worn pair of shoes, as he turned onto the dusty cobblestones of *Judengasse*, Jewish Street, in Czernowitz's Jewish Quarter.

He rushed past small, drab two- and three-family apartment buildings attached to form a single, long structure. Many of the buildings housed small shops featuring a potpourri of Yiddish signs; *katsev* (butcher), *kandelmaker* (candlemaker), *shuster* (cobbler). The building facades began mere inches from the winding street, leaving precious little room to avoid the horse-drawn wagons that were beginning to rattle along – even at this early hour. He dodged the coal wagon, its heavy wheels coated with the muck that constantly accumulated in the gutter, before arriving at a modest storefront. A small wooden sign above the doorway read *Shpayzkrom* (grocery).

He removed a key from his pocket and slipped through the front door, doing his best to prevent the old hinges from creaking. He crossed the tiny room in a matter of seconds, past empty barrels, wooden trestle tables, and crates. Shelves lining the wall were filled with glass jars of jam, oil, tallow, and honey. A simple table at the far end of the shop, next to a sizable ice box, served as the register counter. Yankel gingerly ascended the narrow staircase at the rear of the store. He slowly turned the knob of the door at the top of the stairs and crept inside, turning around to gently close the door.

A throat cleared behind him.

Yankel spun around with a start.

Zushe was sitting on one of the room's five plain wooden chairs. He sipped tea from a tin cup, his long legs crossed in front of him. A candle burned on the table, illuminating the wry look on his face.

"*A guten morgen*," Zushe said quietly. "Had fun in the woods last night?"

Yankel sighed. He was annoyed at having been caught by Zushe again, especially when he lacked the energy to argue. Arguing wasn't his strong suit anyway; he hated conflict of any kind. He grabbed a cup from a shelf and poured himself tea from the kettle, moving quietly so as not to wake five-year-old Hirsch on his mattress at the end of the room. He sat down next to Zushe and began to sip his tea. "I know what you're going to say Zushe, but it won't change my mind."

Zushe uncrossed his legs. "Forget about the socialists and *maskilim*, intellectuals, who go to those Zionist meetings. It is your business if you want to surround yourself with those kinds of *treifedike*, unsuitable, influences. The more pressing matter is that these meetings are dangerous. What if you're seen sneaking around the city by some of those fascist thugs? Or a Jew-hating policeman. You could be killed! What would I say to *Mamme* and *Tatte*?"

Yankel was silent. It was true that the monthly Betar meetings he attended in the nearby Horeczaer Forest were frequented by Reform, socialist, and secular Jewish youths in addition to Orthodox youngsters like himself. His family was devoutly traditional and firmly opposed to the burgeoning Eastern European Socialist movement. But that didn't bother him. He didn't feel that his own strict observance of Torah law was incompatible with his ability to learn from young men and women of different backgrounds. And there was so much to learn! He was educated at the local one-room *heder* (religious Jewish school), whereas many of his fellow Zionists were enrolled at the local public schools. Some even attended university. From them, Yankel learned about history, politics, and literature. Many spoke Russian and German in addition to Romanian. He had a talent for languages. Through conversing with the youths and borrowing some of their books, he learned to passably speak those languages, in addition to ritual Hebrew and the Yiddish he spoke at home. As far as Yankel knew, he was the only Jew in Bukovina who spoke all the Jewish and gentile tongues of the region.

But more importantly, Betar youths shared a common purpose that transcended the relatively minor differences in observance, politics, and education. Each one harbored a deep ardor for the land of Israel and hoped for the establishment of a national Jewish home. Even the youngsters who did not grow up in the poverty and decay of the Jewish Quarter could not avoid the vicious antisemitism that pervaded Romania. To ethnic Romanians, Jew-hatred was as natural as breathing. Radical students and fascist sympathizers could beat, harass, and rob Jews with near impunity.

In 1926, in a Czernowitz courtroom, a young Romanian man named Nicolae Totu pulled a revolver on David Falik, a Jewish student protesting antisemitic professors. Totu put three bullets in Falik's belly. Upon Falik's death, the killer was paraded through town by his friends, adorned with ribbons and the flag of Romania. Octavian Goga, the Romanian Minister of Interior, publicly dubbed Totu a "National Hero". A member of parliament commended Totu for killing one of Romania's "filthy beasts" and called upon every Romanian household to hang an icon of the boy in their homes. Predictably, the incident kicked off a rash of anti-Jewish riots. Jews were beaten in the streets, Jewish stores were looted, and synagogues were set afire.

Antisemitism was the *raison d'etre* of the Iron Guard, a political party with growing influence in the country. Romanians blamed Jews for a whole host of socials ills, including socialism, syphilis, poverty, prostitution, alcoholism, and homosexuality. It was well-known that Adolf Hitler, the leader of Germany's fiercely nationalistic National Socialist party, adopted many of the tactics and symbols of the Iron Guard and their members, the Legionnaires.

At the Betar meetings, the attendees talked about fulfilling their people's millennia-old dream of returning to their ancestral homeland. In the case of Yankel and the other Orthodox Jews, it was a dream they prayed for three times a day while facing south toward the land of Israel. They planned their escape from under the fascist jackboot to live as free Jews in a new, revitalized Israel. This dream was slowly beginning to look like a real possibility. Ever since the Balfour Declaration of 1917, afflicted Jews from all over Europe, individually and in groups, started to make their way toward the Mediterranean. These intrepid settlers dug up stumps, drained swamps, and fought malaria. Pioneer communities, through endless, punishing labor, raised crops from the swampland and cultivated the barren desert. These *halutzim* toiled day and night, leading hard lives in spartan conditions, but they lived as proud, free Jews. Yankel's ancestors had prayed for this opportunity for two thousand bitter years. Now, he and his friends had the chance to make those dreams a reality.

Yankel and his comrades lit bonfires, sang Zionist songs and listened to speeches by local Zionist leaders, while absorbing the Zionist philosophy of liberty, self-reliance, and political autonomy. They studied agricultural methods and exercised their bodies in preparation for their own hoped-for emigration. Occasionally *fusgeyers,* travelers who journeyed to Israel on foot, passed through Czernowitz and joined the meetings in the forest. The *fusgeyers* captivated the young Zionists with tales of their travels and plans upon their arrival in the Holy Land. Yankel yearned for the day when he, too, would join the ranks of the *fusgeyers* and do his part to settle the Land and make the desert bloom. In the meantime, he was content to endure the occasional sleepless night and Zushe's stern looks.

Zushe watched his younger brother engrossed in thought and couldn't resist a slight smile. He understood

Yankel's attachment to the idea of the Holy Land, but he worried for his safety. After all, he was only 15 years old and a small, slight 15-year-old at that. Zushe sighed, placed his cup on the table and stood up. He was nearly six feet tall, broad in the shoulders, and well-built. He was four years older but many inches taller. "Grab your *tefillin*, little brother. It's time for *shacharis*."

The brothers walked up the street, cracking jokes and laughing as they approached the *shtiebel*, the small basement synagogue where the family prayed. Yankel took his usual place toward the back of the room. His father was already there, wrapped in his *tefillin* and prayer shawl, reading intently from the Book of Psalms. He made a point of arriving for services early and insisted that his sons follow suit. The saintly rabbi of the congregation, Rabbi Shlomo Czernowitzer, swayed gently to the prayers at his small wooden table near the Torah ark at the front of the room. Yankel's friend Velvel, a round-faced, good-natured boy with whom he had attended *heder*, smiled at him from a few tables away. Velvel was a fellow Betar member and had also spent the night in the forest. His eyes were red-rimmed from lack of sleep. Yankel wondered if he looked as tired as his friend.

When prayers ended, Yankel headed with his father and brother to the *Judenplatz*, the Jewish market at the intersection of *Judengasse* and *Springbrunnengasse*. By this time of morning, the market was a cacophony of sights, smells, and sounds. Wagons carrying every kind of local good and produce rattled by. Men with long beards, side locks, and black caftans hawked their wares. Ukrainian peasant women in white kerchiefs unloaded crates of squawking chickens. *Shokhtim*, ritual slaughterers, plied their trade right on the street, scattering blood and feathers all about. A burly, mustachioed Romanian policeman in a dark uniform and a helmet sporting an ornate white feather, kept watch over the proceedings, a supercilious look on his face, unaware of the small Jewish boys tying his shoelaces together. *Judenplatz*, as usual, was full of life.

Yankel, Zushe, and their father stopped at old Mendel's cart where day-old baked goods were sold. They picked out a few stale rolls for breakfast – it was all they could afford. Zushe wrapped his roll in wax paper provided by Mendel and took his leave. Zushe was apprenticed to a local tailor and had a long day of work ahead of him. Together with his father, Yankel began to walk home.

"I'm not sure we'll have time to study Talmud later, Yankel," his father said. "Uncle Berel sent word that he plans to come by this evening."

Yankel was relieved, but he didn't let it show. He enjoyed studying with his father but poring over the ancient legal texts required copious mental energy, and he hadn't slept in twenty-four hours. He wasn't sure how he would make it through the day, but he was also excited to see his uncle. You could always count on Uncle Dov Ber, or Berel, to bring interesting news from the provinces.

They entered the shop and climbed the wooden staircase in the rear to reach the main room of their modest home, which served as kitchen, dining area, and bedroom for the three brothers. Yankel's mother was bent over, helping Hirsch pull up his stockings. Hirsch smiled brightly at Yankel.

"*A guten morgen, Mamme,*" Yankel said, "We brought some rolls."

Yankel's mother looked up at him, noting his

exhausted appearance, but she said nothing. He suspected that his parents knew about his nocturnal adventures, but so far, they hadn't given him any trouble about it.

His mother retrieved a dish from a wooden shelf and began to spread butter on Hirsch's roll. "It's a good thing Berel is coming today. This is the last of our butter," she said.

Yankel and his parents poured themselves the remaining tea that Zushe had brewed earlier and sat down to eat.

His parents were gentle people, known for their humility and piety. Yankel's father, Shloime, lost his mother as a young boy. Shloime's father remarried when Shloime was a teenager and his new wife had no interest in raising her stepson. She sent him off to study in *yeshiva*, a Talmudic seminary, where he lived a life of abject poverty, applying himself to his studies and prayers. A man passing through the town joined the yeshiva for the morning *shacharis* services. He was so impressed by the fervent manner of his praying that he offered the hand of his daughter Tzipporah in marriage. Shloime's new father-in-law set up Shloime and Tzipporah with a little shop in Czernowitz, where they started a family.

When Zushe was an infant, a Russian Jew, a refugee of the Great War, found his way to *Judengasse*. The man had lost his entire family, home, and livelihood. He was leprous and deathly ill. Everyone was afraid to approach him. Shloime and Tzipporah took him in, gave him a bed, and fed him until he died shortly thereafter. Since he did not have any children to carry on his legacy, Shloime and Tzipporah agreed to name their next son after him. They were true to their word and named their next son Yakov

Yisroel. They called him Yankel, the Yiddish diminutive of Yakov.

Yankel finished his roll, recited the post-meal benediction, and headed downstairs with his parents and Hirsch. He donned a burlap apron and began filling the store's trestle tables with russet apples, potatoes, onions, and other produce from sacks in the small storeroom in the rear of the shop. Customers began to trickle in, mostly *balebustes,* housewives, buying ingredients for their families' meager dinners. The store quickly emptied of the remaining dairy products; they would not be able to replenish until Uncle Berel arrived. The day dragged on. Yankel assisted shoppers through bleary eyes and suppressed yawns. He really needed some sleep.

Finally, closing time. Yankel helped his father pack up the remaining stock and store them in sacks in the backroom. He straightened out the mason jars on the shelves. Yankel was sweeping the shop floor, still wearing his grocer's apron, when a two-wheeled mule–drawn cart drew to a halt on the cobblestones out front.

"Whoa, there!" Uncle Berel's distinctive baritone carried easily into the store in the autumn air. The man himself followed close behind. Uncle Berel resembled Yankel's father. Both were medium-sized with graying beards. They differed in personality, as much as they were similar in appearance. Where Yankel's father was quiet and reserved, Berel was cheerful and outgoing.

Berel clapped Yankel on the back. "Yankel, my boy!" he bellowed. "What are you still doing sweeping floors like a peasant? How many times do I need to tell you to go to yeshiva already?"

Yankel grinned as he shook Berel's hand. He was always happy to see his uncle, and good-naturedly endured the older man's repeated exhortations for him to become a full-time student. Yankel had a knack for studying the Talmud and its myriad commentaries, and he enjoyed studying it with his father on an almost daily basis. Oftentimes, the lantern at the *shtiebel* sputtered out while father and son were animatedly arguing about the interpretation of one of the finer points of the ancient legal code. Berel, himself an accomplished scholar, had hopes that Yankel would enroll in the great yeshiva in Kamenetz, in Belarus. Uncle Berel was doomed to disappointment. His parents didn't have the funds to support him in yeshiva. He couldn't work at his parents' grocery store forever, either. He figured he'd probably follow Zushe into the tailor trade.

Yankel's father emerged from the storeroom and greeted his brother. The three of them went outside and began unloading crates full of milk, eggs, butter, and cheese that Berel had brought from his dairy farm outside the city. They stored the goods in the icebox and headed upstairs where Tzipporah was preparing a repast of potatoes, onions, and barley.

They were soon joined by Zushe, home from the tailor shop, and dug into the simple meal. Tzipporah inquired about Berel's wife and children, and Shloime asked about this year's farm yield. Berel answered their questions with good cheer and updated them on the happenings in the suburbs. The conversation, as always, eventually turned to politics.

Berel turned somber. "Elections are coming up, you know," he said, "Word is The Iron Guard has the opportunity to pick up a number of seats. People are nervous about what Codreanu will do if he rises to power." Yankel had heard of Corneliu Codreanu, the movie-star handsome leader of the Iron Guard who had attained mythical status among Romania's far-right elements. Codreanu hated Jews with such zeal that he provoked the ire of King Carol II, a liberal leader with a part-Jewish mistress and many Jewish friends.

Tzipporah looked alarmed, but Shloime kept his eyes trained on his plate. "The king will never let that *roshe*, villain, become Prime Minister," Shloime said evenly. "Carol hates those antisemitic *meshugenes*."

Berel sighed. "I hope you're right, brother, but if Codreanu allies with the National Christian Party, the king may not have a choice."

Tzipporah shook her head, her wide eyes betraying her nerves. "The Iron Guard and the National Christians hate each other. They will never join forces."

Berel shot his sister-in-law a sidelong glance. "Yes, they do hate each other," he said. "But they hate us even more."

A sobering silence set over the gathered family as they absorbed his warnings. Berel cleared his throat and began to wipe barley residue off the front of his frock coat with a handkerchief. "Don't worry too much," he said, "if things get rough in the city, you can always come stay on the farm until it blows over. For now, I have to be heading back."

Yankel read the papers anxiously as Romania's governing elite jockeyed for power, the fate of the country's Jews held in the balance. As Uncle Berel had feared, the Iron Guard did pick up a number of seats in parliament in the autumn of 1937 - 156 seats to be exact – cementing its place as Romania's third largest political party. The National Liberal Party, the largest in the country, did not win enough seats to form a government. King Carol was faced with the task of appointing the new prime minister.

To the deep consternation of Romania's Jewish community, Carol chose to appoint as Prime Minister Octavian Goga, head of the fourth-place National Christian Party and champion of the murderer Totu.

Goga was an incompetent prime minister, and he carried out his Jew-hating agenda with such focused zeal that he triggered an economic crisis. Jewish craftsmen fled the countryside and flooded cities like Czernowitz with refugees. Jewish merchants stopped selling their wares and businesses collapsed. In a panic, Romanian Jews began to withdraw their money from banks, which, in turn, caused non-Jewish Romanians to panic and do the same. Goga did not seem to notice; he was entirely occupied with making life as difficult for Jews as was in his power.

Goga and his deputy, Professor Alexandru Cuza, lost no time putting their hateful views into practice. Jewish journalists were denied press privileges and Jewish taverns stripped of their liquor licenses. Yiddish and Hebrew-language newspapers were shuttered. Jewish public servants were dismissed, and public aid to Jewish institutions was withdrawn. Yiddish was banned from use as an official language. A number of valuable Jewish-owned properties were seized.

Finally, the Goga-Cuza government set their sights on the Jewish denizens of Bukovina (where Yankel and his family resided), Bessarabia, and Transylvania. These regions had been annexed from Russia and Austria following the Great War. These districts were home to hundreds of thousands of Jews who were granted Romanian citizenship in 1923. Goga, Cuza and their ilk viewed these newcomers as a grave threat to the purity of the Romanian bloodline. On January 22, 1938, the government officially designated the Jews of the annexed territories as "foreigners", stripping them of their rights as Romanian citizens and all the legal protections conferred by that status.

Yankel noticed the effect on the Jewish Quarter almost immediately. Shops were boarded up. The *Judenplatz* was emptied of produce stands. Beggars lined the streets. Customers came to the grocery store and asked for produce on credit. The Wiesenfeld-Reiners' already meager income dried up. They made do with the help of

Zushe's modest apprentice earnings and by selling dairy products provided by Uncle Berel. Tzipporah fretted about what to feed Hirsch. The little boy, like Yankel, was slight of build. Yankel marveled that his five-year-old brother, certainly feeling the ubiquitous pinch of hunger, never complained.

Anti-Jewish violence erupted in Czernowitz. Goga and Cuza's blue-shirted enforcers, the *Lancieri,* tore through the streets of the city, throwing Jews off trolleys, destroying Jewish businesses, and sowing terror in the Jewish community. Czernowitz's Jews stayed inside, talking in hushed tones, experiencing a uniform sense of dread. They walked outdoors only when absolutely necessary, moving at a fast clip to minimize their vulnerability on the desolate cobblestone-streets. The empty synagogues and study halls waited for worshippers too afraid to leave their homes. Yankel and his father continued their Talmud studies in the family's second-story flat.

Forty-four days after Goga was appointed, Carol dissolved the Goga-Cuza government and seized emergency powers. Carol had a new constitution drafted and signed into law and installed himself as dictator. Carol had Codreanu arrested and moved to suppress the Iron Guard. The king then had Codreanu and several other Iron Guard officials strangled to death in prison while awaiting trial. The official story was that the prisoners were shot while trying to escape.

Romania's Jews breathed a sigh of relief. Slowly, Jewish tradesmen reopened their shops and Jewish merchants began to peddle their wares. Customers trickled back into the Wiesenfeld-Reiner grocery store. Any hope Jews held that their citizenship would be reestablished, however, was quickly dashed. Carol was more concerned with holding onto power than protecting his Jewish subjects. It was becoming increasingly clear that Romania was no longer safe for Jews.

Throughout this time, he continued to sneak off to Betar gatherings in the nearby Horeczaer Forest with his friend Velvel. The desire to immigrate to Palestine grew more fervent with each passing month as the danger in the streets grew. Their songs celebrating the Holy Land reached a fever pitch. Several members of Yankel's group joined the *fusgeyers* and departed for the Levant, heavy packs on their backs. Yankel dreamed of joining them, but he knew he couldn't leave just yet. His parents needed his help in the store, and he was still just a boy. He contented himself to dream, and worked to improve his Russian and Ukrainian language skills.

Meanwhile, to the west, Hitler was on the march.

3

German forces stormed Poland in September of 1939. Twenty-five years had elapsed since Germany capitulated to Allied forces at the culmination of The Great War. The victors dealt Germany a heavy hand. Germany was stripped of territories and forced to pay heavy reparations. Germany, which had lost a full three percent of its population during the conflict, entered a period of severe economic depression and international repudiation. A deep sense of national resentment simmered.

The resentment reached a boiling point when Austrian Adolph Hitler, a former art student and Great War veteran, rose to power at the head of the Nazi party. Hitler seized control of the government from the impotent Weimar Republic in 1933 and established the regime he called the Third Reich. Hitler played on the latent anger of the German people to advance his vision of racial supremacy, militarism, and world domination. Borrowing from his allies in Romania's National Christian Party, Hitler adopted the swastika as his emblem and instituted a series of anti-Jewish measures. He built up Germany's military and, upon the invasion of Poland, publicized his imperialist goals and defied the civilized world.

German Panzer tanks made short work of Poland's mounted cavalry. For eighteen horrific days the cutting-edge tanks mowed down Polish horses and horsemen and brought the country to heel.

The conquest of Poland complete, the *Führer* turned his gaze towards France. At the time, France's army was regarded as the most powerful in Europe. Many Europeans, including the Francophile Romanian elite, expected the French to put an end to Hitler's global ambitions. They were doomed to disappointment. Germany invaded France in May of 1940. The German *Wehrmacht* bulldozed French forces that were still fighting using outdated World War I tactics. They were no match for the Germany *Blitzkrieg*. Six weeks after the invasion, Hitler was photographed walking in front of the Eiffel Tower.

Germany's victory in France shocked the world and utterly changed the political calculus in Romania. The Romanian elite was heavily discredited, providing an opening for the pro-German Iron Guard. The Iron Guard maintained a strong relationship with Germany and began to make the case that they were best-suited to lead the country in the new German-dominated era. Increasingly, the people of Romania agreed.

4

"**D**id you hear the news?!"

Zushe burst into the apartment so suddenly that Tzipporah almost dropped the potato stew she was preparing for dinner. Hirsch looked up in surprise from his seat at the kitchen table.

"Zushe!" Tzipporah scolded, "I could have been burnt!"

"But *Mamme*," Zushe beseeched, "the Russians have invaded!" He waved a newspaper in the air.

Shloime jumped up from his seat, startling little Hirsch. "What did you say? Let me see." Shloime grabbed the newspaper and pushed his bowl and spoon aside to make room on the table.

The whole family crowded around, peering over Shloime's shoulder as he stared at the front page. Shloime looked back up. "This is a Russian paper. Zushe, how do you know what it says?"

Zushe shrugged his wide shoulders. "The constable at the *Judenplatz* told me."

"Yankel, read this out loud." Shloime pushed the paper over to the eighteen-year old.

Yankel furrowed his brow. His Russian was steadily improving, but it still did not come to him as well as his native Yiddish. Since the Yiddish papers had been banned, however, he found himself regularly applying his linguistic talents to decipher the Russian and Ukrainian papers. He focused on the front page. "It's true, the Soviets are taking over Bessarabia and northern Bukovina."

"That includes us!" Tzipporah exclaimed. "Oh, *barukh Hashem,* thank God."

"They didn't invade, though," Yankel clarified. "They threatened to invade if Romanian troops don't withdraw. The Kremlin claims that Northern Bukovina and Bessarabia are Ukrainian territories by right. The paper says that Carol can't rely on France to protect him, so he capitulated. We're being absorbed into the Soviet Union."

The family broke into peals of relieved laughter. Shouts of joy began to filter in from *Judengasse* as word got around the Jewish Quarter. The Romanians are leaving! The *akhzorim,* the cruel ones, are scurrying away! The Legionnaires can't touch us now!

The relief was palpable. There was no love lost between the Jews of Romania and the Soviet government, but anything was better than the brutal treatment at the hands of the Romanian military and the Legionnaires. The very next day, Romanian troops stationed in Czernowitz began their withdrawal. The Jews remained in their homes, but the occasional jeer could be heard above the *stomp stomp stomp* of retreating soldiers.

The Red Army wasted no time in replacing the Romanian military. Jews lined the streets and cheered as the olive-clad infantrymen marched through Czernowitz.

Little girls ran to give the soldiers flowers, and boys shook their hands. The soldiers accepted the attention in good humor, laughing and waving at the townsfolk.

Over the next few days, thousands of German nationals, who had resided in Czernowitz since the Austro-Hungarian occupation, packed their belongings and departed, destined for Germany or Austria. Equal numbers of ethnic Romanians streamed from the city, fearing harsh treatment under the Soviet regime. For the first time in the city's history Jews comprised a majority of the population.

5

Whatever joy the Jews of Czernowitz felt at the arrival of the Soviets was short-lived. The NKVD, the Russian secret police, launched a reign of terror against the Jewish community, targeting them as anti-socialist, bourgeoisie, and Zionist. The screams of women and children whose husbands, fathers, and brothers were dragged from their homes rent the air of *Judengasse* each night. Sleep was out of the question for Yankel. He lay awake, wide-eyed, and wondered how Hirsch never cried.

Betar meetings in the forest were impossible now. Capture by a patrol spelled immediate deportation to a Siberian gulag. The father of Velvel was accused of being a Zionist sympathizer and was loaded onto a train with hundreds of other Jews and sent north. Velvel hadn't heard from him in months.

Meals at the Wiesenfeld-Reiner home took on a funereal air. Parents and children ate their food in silence, faces drawn and grey, brows furrowed with worry. Yankel and his father no longer studied Talmud at the *shtiebel* –

the NKVD had a terrifying habit of hauling men from synagogues and hurling them into the backs of trucks, never to be seen again. His evenings were now dedicated to helping in the grocery and reading books in Russian, Ukrainian, and German. He no longer consumed any material with a Zionist or capitalist bent; it was too risky. But he still read books on history, politics, and economics. Yankel sensed his language skills growing ever stronger. As far as he knew, he was the only person in *Judengasse* to know so many languages.

During the day, Yankel apprenticed with Feivish, the old tailor, a position previously held by Zushe. Now 21 years old, Zushe was employed as a journeyman tailor in another shop closer to the center of town. Feivish was a kind, if brusque, old man, deeply devout, who wore a long white beard that spilled over the front of his waistcoat. The tailor could be sharp with Yankel at times, but he was generally patient. The old man would sit at his work-bench, his stooped shoulders bringing his eye level to his needle and thread. From this position, he had the habit of glancing over the top of his spectacles to check on Yankel's progress, to see whether the young apprentice was cutting a piece of fabric or repairing a minor tear. Feivish barked the occasional criticism, but he mostly trusted him and allowed him a great deal of autonomy.

Yankel, for his part, found that he rather enjoyed the work. He would finger each piece of fabric that passed in front of him, familiarizing himself with the warp and woof the differences in cut and quality. Working silently in Feivish's shop brought him a measure of peace and a sense of stability in an increasingly ominous world.

In this manner he spent the summer of 1940. Many hours each day were occupied by his work in Feivish's shop, focusing on his craft, steadily developing the beginnings of fabric expertise. What time he could spare was spent at the grocery, reading his books and studying Talmud with his father. And he prayed. He prayed that this wave of terror, like so many before it, would run its course. He prayed for the day when he could return to the *shtiebel* and study without fear. He prayed for the day that the Jews of Czernowitz would lose the haunted, hunted look in their eyes and shop at the grocery with the light-heartedness of free men. By the end of the summer, that day's arrival could not have seemed more distant.

Uncle Berel's two-wheeled mule-cart was parked outside the grocery one July evening when Yankel returned to the apartment on *Judengasse*. His heart sank. It seemed each of Berel's visits these days brought more tales of suffering endured by Romania's Jewish community. He used to look forward to seeing his uncle, a learned man who, despite his rural environment, kept himself well-informed of developments in the news. Now the sight of Berel's little mule-cart filled him with dread. He steeled himself, entered the grocery and ascended the stairs to the family home.

When he saw the looks on the faces of his family members he knew his fears were well-founded. His mother looked at him, her face drawn. "Yankel," she said, "Berel brings news from Dorohoi."

He was confused. "Dorohoi? But that's in the Old Kingdom. Isn't it?"

Dorohoi District was a heavily Jewish area in southern Bukovina, a region of the Old Kingdom. The Old Kingdom referred to pre-Great War Romania before the addition of northern Bukovina, Bessarabia, and Transylvania. Many of the Jews of the Old Kingdom still held citizenship and were generally perceived as more "Romanian". Historically, Old Kingdom Jews were subject to greater political protection than the Jews of the outlying provinces.

Berel cast him a wan look. "The savages don't care about kingdoms. To them, a Jew is a Jew, regardless of location."

Berel then repeated what he had just told Shloime and Tzipporah.

His heart was seized in an icy grip when he heard what had transpired in Dorohoi. His mother stood up and busied herself readying little Hirsch for bed. She couldn't bear to hear the story a second time.

Two brigades of the Romanian army were stationed in the Dorohoi District. The soldiers, humiliated that they were forced to peaceably cede the outlying provinces to the Soviets, sought a scapegoat. Antisemitic rumors of Jewish support for the Soviets abounded in Romania. The frustrated soldiers saw the perfect target for their impotent rage in the Jewish community.

The non-Jews of the area were forewarned, Berel told. The soldiers went door-to-door notifying the Christians of their vengeful plan. The Christians raised Romanian national flags and placed crosses on their doors and in their windows so the marauders would pass and leave the occupants unmolested.

On July 1, the slaughter commenced. Mobs of soldiers tore through town, raping, murdering, and looting indiscriminately. In their bloodlust, Romanian soldiers cut off ears, genitals, breasts. They bashed in the heads of children and old people. One man's beard was set aflame.

Jews were hurled from moving trains as passengers watched. Soldiers stormed the funeral of Iancu Solomon, a Jewish soldier who perished in a skirmish with the Red Army. An honor guard of ten Jewish soldiers were lined against a wall and shot. The rest of the attendees were herded into the forest, lined up before a ditch, and executed. A local brigade was called in to put a stop to the butchery. Instead, they joined in.

In nearby Suceava, the rabbi and his sons were tortured and killed. The rabbi's wife was murdered while she prayed. A man was brutalized and then tied to a horse's tail to be dragged through the cobblestone-streets.

Thirty-six Jews were rounded up in Zaharesti. The soldiers cut off tongues, ears, and fingers. They were led to a pit and shot. Some Jews were forced to participate in the firing squad. A dead horse was hurled onto the Jewish corpses filling the pit. The commander brought along his daughter to watch the show.

The worst of the slaughter occurred in the border town of Galati, where 400 Jews attempted to flee to the Soviet Union. They were spotted by a Romanian army unit and massacred.

All this occurred not forty miles from Czernowitz.

The small apartment was deathly silent when Berel finished his tale.

After a couple of minutes, he spoke. "Shloime," Berel said. "My offer to come stay on my farm stands."

6

The surrender of Bessarabia and northern Bukovina proved to be the final straw for the people of Romania. King Carol, with his anti-Hitler and pro-French proclivities, had lost all credibility. Pressure mounted for Carol to step down and allow the Nazi-allied Iron Guard more influence in government affairs. Anti-elite protests erupted in the capital city of Bucharest. Carol desperately cast about for a compromise figure, someone with ties to the Iron Guard but who was also a monarchist and would not call for the King's ouster.

Carol found his man in Ion Antonescu, a lifelong soldier renowned for his ruthlessness. He was nicknamed Red Dog due to his malicious disregard for human life and his red hair. Antonescu had served as Goga's Defense Minister in 1937. He was dismissed by King Carol in 1938 due to his sympathies for the Iron Guard and was later arrested for his attempts to undermine the Carol government.

Antonescu's attitude toward the Jewish community

was hateful, but complicated. When Antonescu was a boy, his father left his mother to marry a Jewish woman. It was said that young Ion blamed his stepmother for breaking up his family, and she informed his lifelong hatred for the Jewish people. That said, Antonescu had Jewish school-mates and, as an officer in the Great War, Antonescu witnessed tens of thousands of Romanian Jews fight and die for their country. These same Jewish fighters who died defending Romania were subjected to horribly anti-semitic conditions at the hands of their fellow soldiers. While serving as a military attaché in Paris in the 1920s, Antonescu was briefly married to Rasela Mandel, a woman of Jewish extraction. Rasela bore Antonescu a son who died in infancy. Antonescu divorced his wife before returning to Romania, where he married a socialite named Maria Niculescu. When the two met in Paris, Maria was married to a French Jew. Indeed, rumor had it that Maria's divorce from her Jewish husband was never finalized.

Antonescu's not-insignificant exposure to Jewish people did nothing to curb his viciously nationalistic anti-Semitism. He believed that Jews were invaders who conspired against Romania. He blamed the Jews for stealing Romania's wealth and viewed them as Romania's most dangerous enemy. To Antonescu, the Jew was evil incarnate. The only solution was expulsion or death.

In Antonescu, Carol saw a man who would help preserve his faltering reign. It was true that Antonescu's pro-Iron Guard bona fides were unimpeachable, and that he harbored a lifelong hatred for democracy and the monarchy. At the same time, he was a member of the elite. Carol gambled that Antonescu could be trusted to uphold the interests of the pro-French aristocracy and keep the rising forces of populism at bay. Carol rolled the dice. Under intense pressure from Germany, Carol recalled Antonescu from his imprisonment at the Bistriţa Monastery in Bukovina (which unbeknownst to the king, Antonescu had already deserted) and in September 1940, appointed him prime minister.

Immediately upon his appointment, Antonescu seized upon rumors that he was under threat of assassination by two of Carol's generals and staged a putsch. With the support of the Iron Guard, Antonescu forced Carol to abdicate the throne and sent the former monarch and his mistress, Elena Lupescu, into exile. Antonescu installed Carol's son Michael as a ceremonial monarch. Michael promptly declared Antonescu *Conducator,* Leader, of all Romania.

The *Conducator's* first act was to declare the Iron Guard Romania's sole legal political party. In November 1940, Antonescu traveled to Berlin, where he conferred with Hitler for three-and-a half hours. That same day, Antonescu signed the Tripartate Pact, formally joining Romania to the axis powers as a junior partner to Hitler's plans for world domination. The two primary animating forces of Romania's government became resisting the allied powers and persecuting Romania's Jews.

The Iron Guard wasted no time in setting up the Legionary Police, a secret police force modeled after the German Gestapo. The Legionary police terrorized Romania's Jews using the tactics of their Nazi counterparts. They razed synagogues and Jewish schools. Men and women were dragged from their homes to join forced work detachments. Jewish houses and businesses were seized, creating a homelessness and unemployment crisis within the Old Kingdom Jewish community. The

Legionary Police set up torture centers, often located in repurposed synagogues, where Jews were brought for interrogation. Jews were marched through the streets to these centers with their hands raised. They were lucky if they left with their lives. Many young Jewish women, and men, were sexually abused as well.

The Legionnaires, as members of the Iron Guard were called, loathed the Jewish religion. They therefore directed much of their energy toward religious symbols and figures. Rabbis were targeted for especially cruel treatment and were often subjected to days of slow torture. Jewish gravestones were stolen or destroyed, and Jewish cemeteries were repurposed for agriculture or to park animal-drawn carts.

Antonescu's partnership with the Iron Guard was destined to be short-lived. The Legionnaires distributed stolen Jewish property amongst themselves, which irked Antonescu, who had expected kickbacks to the government. The Legionnaires ignored orders from Antonescu and instead deferred to the part leader, Horia Sima. Tensions between the *Conducator* and Sima simmered. Both parties jockeyed for Hitler's favor.

In January, with Hitler's support and the backing of the Romanian military, Antonescu threw the Iron Guard out of the government and arrested their leaders. The Legionnaires seized the ministry of the interior, police stations and other government buildings and opened fire on soldiers trying to regain these buildings. The Iron Guard, capitalizing on Antonescu's familial history to portray him as a Jewish puppet, spread propaganda claiming the Jews had revolted. They distributed newspapers throughout the countryside calling on Romanians to heed the call and defend their country from Jews and

Freemasons. Each article concluded with the rallying cry, "You know who to shoot." Peasants streamed to Bucharest, Romania's capital and home to the largest Jewish community in the country, to answer the Legionnaires' call.

The mob descended upon the Jewish neighborhoods of Bucharest and commenced an orgy of slaughter, rape, and destruction. Almost every synagogue in Bucharest was burned to the ground, and almost every Torah scroll desecrated and destroyed. Only one synagogue survived, and even then only because the rioters ran out of fuel. Legionnaires set entire blocks of Jewish homes alight. Some of the fires stretched for several kilometers.

Sixty Jews were seized at random and brought to the slaughterhouse; they were hung on hooks and skinned alive. The perpetrators removed the entrails and hung them around the necks of the corpses. The bodies were then labeled, "Kosher Meat". One of the slaughterhouse victims was a five-year-old girl.

The pillagers included a broad cross-section of Romania society. Police officers, labor unions, university and high school students, Gypsies, and criminals all participated with sadistic glee. Women actively participated. Many of them had Jewish men stripped and struck their genitals with blunt objects.

The rioters targeted Jewish women with venomous glee. Many were tied to stakes and shot by firing squads. If they survived, the Legionnaires finished the job by boring into their breasts with drills.

Antonescu, his hatred for Jews overwhelming his instinct towards law and order, allowed the pogrom to proceed unchecked for two days. Finally, the *Conducator* sent in the army to crush the rebellion. The army's superior firepower quickly overwhelmed the Iron Guard, which was disbanded. Hundreds of Jews were killed, and thousands of homes, businesses, and buildings were destroyed.

Sima fled to Germany, and the army seized the Jewish loot for themselves. Antonescu solidified his iron grip on Romania. For the Jews of Romania, the worst was yet to come.

Yankel stood in front of the grocery on *Judengasse* with his family to say goodbye to his little brother Hirsch. Over the last few years, Berel had exhorted them tirelessly to leave the growing dangers of the city behind and join his family on their dairy farm in the countryside. Until now, Shloime and Tzipporah had resisted, but Operation Barbarossa changed their minds, at least as far as their youngest child was concerned.

In a shocking reversal, Hitler betrayed the non-aggression pact he had signed with Stalin in 1939. In late June 1941, three million German soldiers crossed the frontier and smashed into the Soviet Union. Hitler's motivation for the invasion was his perceived need for *Lebensraum,* or living space, for the Aryan citizens of the emerging Nazi empire. He planned to seize the natural resources, conscript slave labor, and ultimately clear western Russia of its Slavic inhabitants. The German fighters were bolstered by hundreds of thousands of Romanian soldiers fielded by Hitler's vassal Antonescu.

The primitive and ill-equipped Red Army was no

match for the most sophisticated fighting force in the world. Soviet Great War-era rifles withered under the barrage of German Panzers, and their untrained fighting force was outmaneuvered by superior German military tactics. The *Wehrmacht,* the Germany army, moved steadily east. It was only a matter of time before they reached Bukovina. The Jews of Bukovina were well aware of how the Germans felt about the Jews.

Shloime and Tzipporah were loath to leave behind their life and business in Czernowitz, but they tearfully concluded that Czernowitz was no place for an eight-year-old boy. They sent to Berel asking him to shelter little Hirsch until the storm passed. Tzipporah dressed her son in his warmest clothes and filled a rucksack with what little supplies she had. Berel made the trip to *Judengasse* in his little mule cart to bring Hirsch home with him.

Tzipporah fussed over her son, buttoning his coat for the umpteenth time, checking his sack to make sure he had enough food for the trip, attempting to mask her true feelings with a false cheerfulness.

Hirsch, always a quiet child, stood silently with downcast eyes. When she couldn't think of anything else to tighten or double-check, Tzipporah embraced her son and told him to behave and not forget his prayers. One by one, Hirsch wordlessly hugged his father and Zushe. When it was his turn, Yankel fought to hold back his tears. "You'll be back before you know it," he choked out. "I'll take you to your first Betar meeting."

Hirsch just nodded. He walked to where Berel was waiting by the cart and solemnly climbed into the rear-facing seat. He waved as Berel goaded the mule into action and the wagon trundled away.

Yankel never saw his brother again.

8

Yankel was jerked from slumber by the sound of a massive explosion that shook the small apartment on *Judengasse* in June of 1941. He and Zushe leapt from their cots and ran to the window. They were quickly joined by their parents. The family watched as the night sky lit up with vivid hues of red and yellow. Fighter planes roared overhead, rapidly firing their mounted machine guns. Soviet soldiers streamed through the streets, loading their weapons and yelling to their comrades.

For two days, the chaos continued as Yankel and his family hunkered down in the small apartment. The sounds of planes, explosions, air raid alarms, and flak fire were constant. Plumes of smoke in the distance were visible from the apartment window. At one point, Zushe crept downstairs to the grocery for provisions. Otherwise, the family sat in silence. Occasionally Zushe or Shloime would attempt to read from a tractate of Talmud. Inevitably, they gave up after a few minutes. The palpable anxiety pervading the home rendered any intellectual activity impossible. Tzipporah prayed ceaselessly from her book of Psalms. Yankel knew she was thinking of Hirsch and wondering how he fared in the countryside. He wished they owned a radio, so they could have an idea of what was transpiring.

On the third day, during a torrential downpour, the Red Army began to flee the city. A long line of tanks, armored cars, artillery, and soldiers headed eastward towards the Russian heartland. They were joined by thousands of civilian refugees heading for the train station or the roads leaving Czernowitz. The roads were clogged with wagons, automobiles, and pedestrians. The cacophony was incessant.

The evacuation and the fighting continued for a week. At midnight on July 1, Yankel and his family heard a series of rapid explosions coming from the east. Then the bombing ceased. A deathly quiet descended upon *Judengasse*. The family conferred about whether to remain sheltered in their apartment or to venture outside. Yankel and Zushe decided to descend to the street; they hungered for news. Shloime and Tzipporah had lived through the Great War and the havoc it wrought. Their curiosity was not so strong. They elected to remain behind in the apartment.

The two brothers waited until dawn broke and slowly descended the stairs and emerged onto the cobblestone-street beyond. Giant clouds of smoke hung over the Jewish Quarter. A few neighbors cautiously crept out of their homes and looked around tentatively. Yankel peered through the smoke and saw a familiar face. "Velvel!" he called out. "Over here!"

Velvel made his way over to the brothers. His normally cheerful demeanor was gone. He'd lost weight. Life had been hard for Velvel's family since his father was sent to

Siberia. Tzipporah had taken to delivering a small package of food to Velvel's mother every Friday before *Shabbos*.

"*Vos iz neias?*" Zushe asked as Velvel drew near. "What news?"

Velvel spread his hands. "I was hoping you could tell me. I've been hiding out for a week."

Yankel and Zushe shot each other disappointed looks. They were hoping not to have to stray too far from their home to gather information. Yankel wished Uncle Berel was there – he was always well-informed. Thinking about Uncle Berel made him think about his brother, and thinking about Hirsch was too painful. He pushed the thought out of his mind.

The three young men decided to hunt down news together. They proceeded towards the Jewish Market where *Judengasse* and *Springbrunnengasse* converged. The number of people milling around the street gradually increased as more people found the nerve to venture outside their homes.

The three friends reached the *Judenplatz*. It was barren of any commerce. The firehouse was a smoldering ruin. The Russians had set it alight before leaving, so the invading army could not make use of the equipment. The many shops and stands lay empty and abandoned. A thick layer of dust covered everything. Mendel's overturned bread cart lay on the cobblestones.

But more depressing than the sight of mass destruction was the sight of the people they passed on the streets. Several Jews, gaunt and in tatters, picked their way among the empty food stands, looking for scraps to eat. One middle-aged man combed the ground around Mendel's cart. He knew he wouldn't find anything.

Yankel and his companions approached the man. "*Shalom aleychem,*" Zushe called out. "Any news about the war?"

The man recoiled and looked up at them, fear in his eyes. His hair was matted with dried blood on one side of his crown. When he saw that Zushe was a fellow Jew he visibly relaxed. Then he began to cry. "You have no idea," the man sobbed. "You have no idea what's coming. I've lost everything. All I have are the clothes on my back. Not even a crust of bread. I will go the way of my poor family." His weeping intensified.

Yankel and Zushe looked at each other again, and Zushe nodded. He turned to the stranger and addressed him, "Come with us," Zushe said. "We might be able to spare some food and a place to sleep."

The man looked grateful through his tears. The four of them made their way back to the grocery store and upstairs to the apartment. Tzipporah looked up as they stepped through the wooden door at the top of the stairs. Relief crossed her face, which gave way to puzzlement when she observed Velvel and their ragged guest. Tzipporah immediately stood up and began to prepare some food and boil tea. Shloime sprang to his feet and offered the stranger his chair. Yankel wet a rag with some water so the man could clean his wound.

The family gathered around the table and waited on tenterhooks as the guest ate and drank his fill. He wasn't a large man, rendered smaller by fear and hunger, and he ate with unnerving desperation. When he was sated, he quietly but intensely recited the post-meal benediction. Then he propped his elbows on the table and began his tale. "My name is Eliyahu Zisman. I am from the *shtetl* of Strozhnitz. I lived there with my wife and two daughters and made a simple living as a cobbler. Every Jew in Strozhnitz hid in their cellar or attic when the bombing began. A few days ago, the Soviet unit that was stationed there evacuated and fled east. No one left their homes. We were all too scared. Within hours a mob descended on our town. Ukrainian and Romanian peasants wielding rifles, clubs, and pitchforks went door-to-door. They dragged Jews outside and beat them mercilessly, and then shot them on the spot. The thugs tore out the men's beards and gouged their eyes. The things they did to the women were unspeakable." Eliyahu's voice caught. He looked down at the table. Then he took a rattling breath and continued.

"Five Romanian gendarmes burst into my home. Two of them held me back while they took turns violating my wife and daughters. When they finished, they stabbed them over and over with their bayonets while the two holding me back laughed. In my state of mad grief, I tore free of their clutches and lunged at the murderers. One of them swung his rifle like a club and struck me in the head. I crashed to the floor in a daze. I lay there with my eyes closed while my tormentors, thinking I was dead, cleared the house of what little provisions and valuables we owned. They finally left and moved on to find new victims. I lay there for a full day playing dead while the pogrom continued. The following night, I fled to the forest. I could hear the rifle cracks as the Jews of the town were lined up and shot. Their bodies were thrown into the ditch we used to dump dead dogs. I hid in the forest for another day before I felt it was safe to flee Strozhnitz. I took the road to Czernowitz. I hoped that the Soviets would try harder to defend a big city. I didn't even have the chance to bury my family." Eliyahu wiped a tear from his eye.

Shloime put a reassuring hand on Eliyahu's shoulder.

"The road to Czernowitz was strewn with Jewish corpses, many of them horribly mangled. I saw the body of a woman with both arms sawn off. I met Jews fleeing scenes of similar brutality in other villages. They told me that the Germans had taken the Soviet stronghold of Lemberg and were bombing the Czernowitz airport and train station. I also heard about the horrible pogrom in the city of Iasi, where Antonescu, who has promoted himself to Marshal, by the way, authorized the wholesale slaughter of the Jewish community. Police officers, townspeople and even Legionnaires freed from prison by Antonescu specifically for the purpose, took part in the butchery. Many thousands were crammed into death trains, one hundred people to a car, departing for destinations unknown. They say fifteen thousand Jews died in Iasi. As I neared Czernowitz, word reached me that the Soviets were fleeing the city. I continued toward the city anyway. I hadn't eaten in two days and I had nowhere else to go. No trains are operating, and the Russians bombed the bridges over the River Prut, cutting off the route east."

Yankel nodded to himself. That explained the rapid sequence of explosions last night.

Eliyahu locked eyes with Shloime. His gaze was hollow. "The peasant mob is making its way across the countryside. It's only a matter of time before they reach Czernowitz. All you can do now is pray."

The apartment was deathly silent when Eliyahu finished speaking. Yankel's heart filled with dread. His mind was blank. He couldn't see a way out for his family.

Shloime broke the silence after a couple of minutes. Zushe, run downstairs and gather food from the store. "We're going to need provisions."

Zushe nodded and stood up.

Velvel followed, his face ashen. "I need to be with my mother. *Hatzlacha,* good fortune, to you all." Velvel hurried out the door after Zushe.

When Zushe returned, the family pushed the small kitchen table against the door. They placed a heavy trunk on top of the table to increase its weight. The Wiesenfeld-Reiner family and their guest remained hidden and waited.

The wait was not long. Within hours, Czernowitz was an inferno. Howling mobs of Ukrainian and Romanian peasants stormed the Jewish Quarter. They wielded clubs, sacks, and torches. Cries of "Kill the Jews!" rent the air. The pillagers smashed into homes and businesses, looting anything of value. What they couldn't take they destroyed. Jewish homes were set afire. Yankel could see the flames through the apartment window. Eventually, the buildings would fall with a deafening boom. Any Jew unlucky enough to be caught outside was shot on the spot, his body left lying in the street for stray dogs.

The first night, they came for the shop. The Wiesenfeld- Reiners sat perfectly still in their second-floor apartment and held their breath. They heard the sound of cursing, heavy boots, and broken glass; drunken laughter as trestles were overturned and tables broken. Yankel thought he could make out the sound of turnips spilling onto the floor. Eliyahu sat on his cot, his arms clenched tightly around his knees, tears streaming silently from behind eyes screwed tightly shut.

For a terrifying few seconds, they could hear someone rattling the doorknob of the door at the bottom of the stairs. The rattling ceased, and shortly thereafter the rioters lost interest. They departed and made their way up the street, their wild yells echoing across the cobblestones.

The looting continued for five days. On July 6, the German Army entered the city. German command gave the soldiers three days to loot, rape, and kill with impunity. The soldiers, their appetite for blood whetted by battle, gleefully complied. The terror intensified. Yankel and his family did not budge from their apartment. No one slept.

Screams of pain and terror were their constant companions. The Gestapo, along with *Einsatz Gruppe* D mobile Jew-killing squads, commandeered the Black Eagle Hotel as their headquarters. German soldiers went door to door, raping the women and taking whatever they pleased. Rabbis, community leaders, and members of the intelligentsia were arrested, as was anyone who could not provide papers. Many were arrested for no reason at all. They were marched to the police station, a target range, or a courtyard and shot. The Nazis torched every synagogue in Czernowitz.

Einsatzkommandos dragged Rabbi Abraham Mark, the Chief Rabbi of the city, to the steps of the Great Synagogue of Czernowitz. When the synagogue was built in 1873, it was the grandest building in all Czernowitz. Rabbi Mark was forced to watch as the Germans burned the building to the ground. They also torched the synagogue's sixty Torah scrolls. Rabbi Mark was then brought to the Black Eagle, where he was tortured for two days along with two cantors and the beadle. They were then shot, along with 160 other Jews, on the banks of the River Prut.

The Nazis came to *Judengasse* on July 7. Yankel heard the terrifying sound of several pairs of jackboots treading over the broken glass in the store downstairs. The doorknob rattled once again, briefly. Then someone barked an order, and the smash of a rifle butt against the knob made the upstairs inhabitants jump. Heavy footsteps pounded up the stairs, and then a heavy fist rapped on the door.

"Open up!"

Yankel's heart leapt into his throat. He had never known such terror. Shloime threw an anxious look at his wife then stood and, with Zushe's help, pushed the table aside. With a shaking hand, Shloime unlatched the door and pulled it open. Yankel got his first look at German soldiers.

There were four of them; they all appeared to be about his age, but tall and well-built. Their green-grey uniforms were pristine, and their legs were clad in high leather boots. They each held a rifle over their right shoulder. They were led by a smaller man in an impeccably tailored suit and fedora. He wore round, gold-rimmed spectacles and a white handkerchief folded in a neat square in his jacket's breast pocket. Yankel could not help but notice that his hair was fastidiously combed.

The leader stepped into the small apartment, followed by the soldiers. They took up an incredible amount of space.

Shloime stepped back.

The leader spoke. "Is this the Wiesenfeld-Reiner residence?"

Shloime nodded numbly.

The man spoke in German, but Yiddish was closely-enough related that he could understand. The man reached into his inside jacket pocket, revealing a shoulder holster and pistol, and retrieved a leather wallet. With a quick gesture, he flipped it open to reveal a copper-colored badge. Yankel could just make out an insignia composed of an eagle atop a swastika above the words, "*Geheime Staatspolizei*", before the agent returned the badge to his jacket.

"My name is Herr Metzger. Kindly furnish your papers," the Gestapo agent said to Shloime.

Shloime haltingly moved to the chest sitting atop the kitchen table and after rifling around for a bit removed a stack of documents. One of the soldiers stepped forward, snatched them from Shloime, and handed them to the Gestapo man.

Metzger scrutinized each document. There were four sets of papers, one for each member of the family present. Time stretched on interminably. At one point, Metzger removed the handkerchief from his pocket, handed the papers to a soldier, and painstakingly cleaned his spectacles before resuming the review. The Wiesenfeld-Reiners stood stock still, afraid to move a muscle. When Yankel felt he could not bear the tension any longer, Metzger handed the papers back to the soldier.

"Everything appears to be in order," he said.

Yankel slowly exhaled. He could feel his family doing the same. The soldier contemptuously tossed the papers onto the floor.

Metzger turned to Eliyahu. The refugee was standing behind everyone else, his head down, his hands clasped before him. "And your papers, sir?" the Gestapo man said.

Eliyahu lifted his head. He had the look of a hunted animal. He spread his hands pleadingly. His mouth worked, but no words came out.

Metzger looked at Eliyahu distastefully. "I see," he said simply. He gestured at the soldiers. Instantly, two of them crossed the room in two powerful strides, shoving

Shloime and Yankel aside in the process. They grabbed each of Eliyahu's arms in a tight grip.

Eliyahu found his voice and started screaming. "No! No! I have papers! I left them in Strozhnitz! Please, I can go back and get them!" Eliyahu dug his feet into the wooden floor and pulled back as hard as he could. But he was no match for the two soldiers. They hauled him to the door with no apparent strain. Eliyahu, still howling, grabbed the doorjamb and clung with all his might.

Metzger narrowed his eyes. He removed a pistol from his shoulder holster. Grasping the gun by the barrel, he rapped Eliyahu's fingers repeatedly. Eliyahu's shrieking intensified but he held on. Metzger kept striking him until the sound of bones cracking were audible.

Eliyahu let go. He was dragged down the stairs, followed by Metzger, who closed the door behind him. The Wiesenfeld-Reiners could hear Eliyahu's screams for what felt like an eternity.

The Holocaust had come to Czernowitz.

9

By July 10, 1940 hiding in the apartment was no longer an option. German and Romanian soldiers went door to door each morning, conscripting Jews for forced labor. Yankel was jerked from his feverish sleep by a loud knock on the door. Zushe, frantically rubbing the sleep from his eyes, opened the door. A Romanian soldier thrust a work order at Zushe. "You have one hour," he barked.

They scanned the document. Yankel was assigned to clear rubble from the city center. To his relief, Zushe would be joining him. Shloime's orders were to report to the Jewish cemetery to help with burial. Tzipporah's job was to clean the home of a wealthy Romanian government official. The family quickly washed, dressed, prayed, and departed for their assigned duties.

The sight that met him as he rushed down *Judengasse* alongside his brother was terrible. Bodies of the dead and wounded littered the streets. A teenage girl, her clothes ripped from her body and blood streaming from her mouth, dragged herself painfully across the cobblestones. Her legs appeared to be broken. Jewish conscripts, their backs bent in submission, carted bodies away on stretchers, wagons, and wheelbarrows. One corpse-laden wheelbarrow bounced along the cobblestones past the brothers. The victim's head lolled over the side of the barrow. It was Feivish, the tailor. His eyes were open in a glassy stare.

Not a window was unbroken; not a single door unsmashed. Every shop and business had been relieved of their cash and wares. Some buildings had been destroyed altogether, leaving piles of rubble in their place. Boys picked through the ruins, looking for valuables. He felt himself go numb. He could not process what he was seeing.

Yankel and Zushe arrived at the city center, where throngs of Jews were already assembled. The brothers reported to the gendarme on duty. He barely looked at them. "Synagogue duty," he spat.

Yankel and Zushe set to work clearing rubble and loading it into waiting trucks. The weight of stone and cement was crushing, even for Zushe. Romanian soldiers stood watch, leaning on their rifles and chatting to each other. Occasionally they hurled abuse or struck the laborers.

After several hours, he was utterly exhausted. There were no breaks, and their tormentors did not provide them with meals. Zushe labored stoically, but Yankel felt himself fading. He stopped to wipe sweat from his brow.

A blow to his side sent him sprawling. He looked up, clutching his ribs, the wind utterly knocked out of him. A huge Romanian gendarme stood over him, retracting the giant booted foot that dealt the blow. Zushe looked on in horror.

"Get back up, Jew," the gendarme growled. "Next time it will be your head." The gendarme spat and walked away.

Zushe pulled Yankel to his feet. "No breaks," Zushe whispered urgently. "Just keep working."

He was certain his ribs were cracked. Every breath was agonizing. But he didn't dare stop working again. Occasionally, Zushe would help him carry some of the larger stones. The hours dragged on.

The same gendarme next turned his attention to a sandy-haired man attempting to break pieces of rubble with a pickaxe. His slight build and spectacles denoted an intellectual. He was not making much progress with his work. The pickaxe kept slipping, and the man's hands were blistered and bloody. The gendarme towered over him. "What's going on, Jew? Breaking rocks is too complicated for you?"

The man looked up beseechingly. "I'm a professor," he pleaded. "I'm not suited for this kind of work. Is there any administrative or office work I can do instead?"

The gendarme leered down at him. "You're right. You are not suited to this work." The gendarme swung his rifle off his shoulder. The professor barely had time to widen his eyes before he was shot point blank.

Yankel's heart thundered in his chest. He dared not stop working.

The gendarme pointed to two laborers at random. "You and you. Throw him in the truck with the rest of the trash." The laborers did as ordered. Their shoes crunched over the dead man's glasses as they carried him to the truck and slung him onto the rocks.

Yankel and Zushe kept their eyes down and kept working.

After twelve hours of work, the laborers were allowed to return home. Yankel and Zushe trudged back to *Judengasse* exhausted and filthy. They dragged themselves upstairs and helped themselves to some of what was left of the food in the apartment. Yankel's ribs ached horribly. They were joined shortly by their parents. Tzipporah looked worn and demoralized, but the expression on Shloime's face filled Yankel with a deep sense of foreboding. His father was ashen. He looked as if he had aged ten years.

"The cemetery is overflowing with the dead," he reported. "We had no choice but to pile them in mass graves. No *tahara*, ritual purification, nothing."

Shloime put his head in his hands. "Thousands of Jews. I had no idea there were that many Jews in Czernowitz to kill."

Life continued in this manner for the remainder of the summer. Each morning, a soldier would bang on the door and issue a work order. The family members would report to their assignments and labor until the guards allowed them to go home. Their food had long since run out. They made do with whatever food Tzipporah was able to salvage from the kitchens of the homes she was forced to clean. Sometimes the maids took pity on her and would slip her some scraps. Others would beat her if she had the temerity to ask.

Yankel was in a perennial state of exhaustion. For weeks he labored despite the throbbing pain in his ribs. He worked constantly, seven days a week. They were not even spared on *Shabbos*, the holy day of rest. Refusal to work meant instant death. When the synagogue area was cleared, Yankel and Zushe were reassigned to the train station to assist in repairs.

The work was dangerous. He had witnessed workers killed by collapsing structures and wayward train cars. He began to lose weight steadily, taxing his already thin frame. Usually, he and Zushe were assigned to work together. Yankel dreaded the days they were separated. He felt more vulnerable than ever.

The *Einsatzgruppen* remained active for over a month, longer than in any other location in Europe. Working relentlessly, they gathered Jews for execution by the hundreds. The sound of their firing squads at work provided a terrifying backdrop to life under Nazi rule. Their activities provided a steady flow of dead bodies for Shloime and the other members of the burial squad. Death, rape, cruelty, and humiliation were constantly present. He found that he was no longer shocked by any of it.

An order came down from the Gestapo in August of 1941. The Jews were given three days to pin a yellow Star of David to the outside of their clothes. Tzipporah dutifully cut pieces of fabric and sewed them onto their increasingly worn garments. Czernowitz' Jews would now be more easily identified for abuse.

Jews were also banned from owning radios and telephones and could only buy food between eight and eleven in the morning. This did not unduly affect the Wiesenfeld-Reiner family. They did not own a radio nor a telephone and they had no money for food. But it was clear that the authorities were waging a campaign to strip the Jewish community of their few remaining rights.

The High Holy Days were a more somber affair than usual that year. There wasn't enough food for the festive meals. On *Yom Kippur*, the day of fasting and repentance, forced labor continued as usual. His father ordered his

family to eat what little food they had. He said it was
important for them to keep their strength. Yankel noticed
that his father did not touch a morsel.

10

A new order was broadcast via megaphone at noon on October 11, 1941. The order came directly from Marshal Antonescu. Every Jew in Czernowitz had six hours to report to the ghetto that would be established in the Jewish Quarter. The penalty for failing to report to the ghetto was death. Jews were permitted to bring what they could carry on their backs. Everything else would be confiscated by the Romanian government. The order went out for the Jews of Czernowitz to deposit all their gold, silver, and valuables at the National Bank.

Chaos ensued as fifty thousand people scrambled to squeeze into a few square blocks in the run-down Jewish Quarter. Panicked Jews ran back and forth, wearing backpacks stuffed to the brim, clutching books, lamps, and pillows in their hands.

Confusion reigned as many Jews did not know precisely where the ghetto was located but were desperate to enter before the deadline. No signs were posted, and no instructions issued. Once they left their homes they were not permitted to return. Policemen guarded the abandoned Jewish houses and shepherded the Jews through the streets, truncheons swinging. Mobs streamed in from the suburbs and plundered the deserted homes.

A ten-foot barbed-wire fence surrounded the ghetto. Mountains of luggage lined the streets of the Jewish quarter as masses of people squeezed in. Romanian soldiers robbed people of boots and fur hats in broad daylight. In the commotion, an eight-year-old boy was crushed under a wagon wheel.

Families were forced to share their small living spaces. Forty, fifty, even a hundred people filled apartments designed for small families. The water pipes to the ghetto were shut off, and toilets clogged almost immediately. Three families moved into the Wiesenfeld-Reiner apartment on *Judengasse*. One family of four from the city center named Rozen were secular Jews who did not speak Yiddish. They were expensively dressed and carried fine leather suitcases. They looked more bewildered than he felt. The two Rozen children stared at him with a mix of curiosity and fear.

Tzipporah, laboring to be hospitable even in these circumstances, assured the Rozen family that they could have the main room of the apartment all to themselves while she and her family would retreat to the bedroom. The Rozens looked around the small apartment, viewing its plain furnishings with dismay.

Two Hasidic families with eleven children between them, all related to one another, were also assigned to the Wiesenfeld-Reiner residence. They lived only a couple of blocks over, just outside the ghetto boundaries, and were used to the simple life. They occupied the barren grocery store on the street level, laying burlap sacks on the floor and wooden tables.

Conditions in the ghetto were horrible. It was forbidden to leave without a permit, which was issued only to doctors in special circumstances. Even they could only leave the ghetto under guard. Food was scarce and hunger abounded. The stench of humanity, sewage, and fear was unbearable. Privacy was nonexistent. Tzipporah hung up a ragged cloth in the bedroom to shield herself while dressing. The claustrophobia was overwhelming as the small home was clogged with people. The already narrow streets of the Jewish Quarter were no better. The old and the crippled begged ceaselessly. They were joined by the mentally disturbed since the staff of Czernowitz' Jewish insane asylum had been slaughtered. The Jews of the ghetto, who had nothing to give, averted their eyes and continued on their way. A dozen people committed suicide every day. People camped in courtyards, on roofs, in hallways, on stairs, in every available corner.

Still, Yankel found ways to bolster his spirits. As a German speaker, he enjoyed talking to the Rozens and learning about their lives. The Rozens, in turn, were grateful that someone in the house spoke their language. They told him all about their former life in an upscale apartment overlooking the German Theatre. Maniu Rozen, the husband, was an executive of a marble company before the war. He and his wife, Rachel, had been educated at the best universities. They and their children had received a Romanian education. They had many German and Romanian friends and never interacted with traditional Jews. When the war erupted, Maniu lost his job and his children were expelled from school. The Rozens' gentile friends utterly abandoned them, turning up only to volunteer to safeguard their valuables when the ghetto was announced. The Rozens did not expect to ever see their valuables again.

Yankel also resumed attending Betar meetings, which had secretly started to meet again in cellars of the ghetto. For obvious reasons emigrating to the Holy Land was out of the question. But the spate of persecution reinforced the young Zionists in their determination to seek their destiny far from the hatred of Europe. When the war was over, they told each other, they would proudly march south to help cultivate the land of their ancestral home.

He attended the meetings with his friend Velvel, whose cheerfulness had long since deserted him. Velvel's mother's health had been in decline ever since her husband's deportation. The deplorable conditions of the ghetto accelerated the process. Velvel's once-round face was now gaunt from hunger and worry.

Yankel, for his part, burned with the desire to settle in *Eretz Yisrael*, the Land of Israel. He dreamed of open spaces far from the putrid streets of Czernowitz. The thought of living openly as a Jew in a Jewish land, rather than cowering in a dank cellar surrounded by enemies, was enough to make his breath catch. For the time being, however, he needed to be content with his imagination. He was deep in Nazi territory. Even if he were to escape the confines of the ghetto there was nowhere for him to go.

11

Rumors rumbled through the ghetto. Within days of the ghetto's establishment, Romanian soldiers began arresting people, irrespective of age, sex, or occupation. Thousands of Jews were herded into wagons and transported to the train station. It was whispered that their destination was Transnistria, the land beyond the Dniester River to the east, the border to the Ukraine. No one was certain as to what befell those sent to Transnistria. What was well-known was that no one ever returned. The very word "Transnistria" was enough to generate panic in the hearts of Czernowitz's Jewish community. Yankel and his family spent each minute in dread of selection.

Five thousand Jews were arrested during the *Sukkoth* festival. Yankel watched as the Bojan Hasidic sect emerged from their synagogue at gunpoint. Clad in their holiday finery, they wordlessly marched toward the train station. Their rabbi, Torah scroll in hand, walked at their head. The two Hasidic families that had camped in the grocery were among those deported.

For the deportees, the scene was one of hysteria. Parents struggled to hang on to their children as guards cracked their whips and swung clubs. The old and the infirm often fell from the blows, never to rise again. One woman, who had given birth three days earlier, was loaded onto a wagon despite her raging fever. By the time the wagon reached the station both she and her child were dead.

Tzipporah spent her days bent over her book of Psalms, praying she and her family wouldn't be next.

Rumors began to circulate again. Mayor Traian Popivici, a good man, who made every effort to protect the Jews of his city, had obtained a reprieve. He had convinced the governor that Jews had skills necessary to maintain commerce. The governor had agreed that Jews who practiced trades deemed essential would be issued temporary permits to remain in Czernowitz. Middlemen emerged, promising access to permits in exchange for huge sums of money. Desperate Jews turned over whatever money they had left to these swindlers and were left more miserable and destitute than ever.

News of the permits spread through the ghetto like wildfire. The Wiesenfeld-Reiners joined the throngs of people streaming toward the Jewish Hospital where essential trade permit registration was being held. They stood in line for an entire day in the Romanian cold until it was their turn to register.

Yankel, who knew Romanian, filled out the occupation forms for all of them. For him and Zushe, he wrote "tailor". He put down "grocer" for each of his parents. The family returned to their crowded apartment to anxiously await the outcome. Yankel caught a look at himself in his mother's mirror. A few of his hairs were turning white. He was not yet nineteen years old.

Several days later, fifteen thousand Jews were issued Popivici permits. Yankel and his family were not among them. The first snow fell.

12

They were deported on October 20. A Romanian soldier knocked loudly on the apartment door early in the morning. The bedroom door opened and Yankel peered out to the main room. The Rozens sat on their cots looking frightened and made no move to rise. Yankel walked to the door and pulled it open. The soldier handed him a paper, turned on his heel, and descended the stairs without another word.

Yankel glanced at the document. The occupants of the apartment had one half hour to pack and report to the *Judenplatz*. The next few minutes were a flurry of activity as the family scrambled to throw anything they could carry into burlap sacks. Yankel's family did not own much more than a few sets of clothes. Tzipporah packed their remaining rations, four bowls and spoons, and a gold necklace, a gift from her parents on the occasion of her wedding. Shloime packed the family papers and their well-worn book of Psalms.

There was no time for morning prayers. "Bring your

tefillin," Shloime told his sons in a low voice. "Hopefully, we'll have time to pray at the station."

The Rozens packed their handsome leather cases, their faces set. They finished quickly, as they had never fully unpacked to begin with. They stood close together in the main room. "Yankel," Maniu Rozen called out.

Yankel approached.

"We won't be joining you on the journey."

Yankel raised his eyebrows in surprise.

"We smuggled some valuables with us from home. We've made contact with a Romanian colleague of mine. He's agreed to hide us until the war is over."

He registered this information. "In exchange for your valuables? Is that the deal?"

Maniu didn't reply. He just offered his hand. "Good luck, Yankel, and thank your parents for everything."

He shook Maniu's hand.

The Rozens left without another word.

Minutes later, the Wiesenfeld-Reiner family quickly made their way along the snow-coated streets to the *Judenplatz*, balancing their luggage as best they could. They joined hundreds of other frightened Jews – traditional, Hasidic, and secular – a single, teeming mass, reeking of fear. The weather was freezing, but he barely noticed the cold. He spied his friend Velvel amidst the throng, supporting his frail mother on his arm.

Herr Metzger, the Gestapo agent, calmly observed the proceedings from atop a wagon on the outskirts of the square, his hands clasped behind his back.

The square was ringed by jackbooted guards armed with rifles, whips, and clubs. They struck people indiscriminately. He saw a small boy fall to the ground, his mouth bleeding from the blow of a rifle butt. The boy's mother pulled him to his feet and kept walking.

More and more Jews poured into the square until Yankel was shoulder-to-shoulder with thousands of people. They were joined by the denizens of the insane asylum and children from the orphanage. The insane were dressed in tatters and howled in fear. It made for a horrible sight. They waited in this manner for an hour.

Then the order came. "Move!" The guards cracked their whips. The Jews in the square were hustled forward. He was forced by the blows of the guards to move at a half-jog. He and his family held on to each other tightly. To fall meant being trampled to death. They struggled not to drop their luggage.

They passed through the barbed-wire fence of the ghetto and were herded through the city. Townspeople lined the streets, clapping and jeering. Some of them threw pieces of rotten fruit. A few starving people risked death and dove to retrieve the refuse. The elderly and infirm who could not keep pace fell to the ground. Mothers clutched howling infants close. Yankel grimly kept marching.

They arrived at the freight station on the banks of the River Prut. The mass of Jews was forcefully prodded into a large waiting area and divided into several lines. At the head of each line was a Romanian official. Each family was required to present their baggage for inspection. The Wiesenfeld-Reiner family did not reach the front of the line for several hours. They were not allowed to sit. Wrapping *tefillin*, the leather phylacteries worn by men during morning prayers, was out of the question. Yankel muttered the prayers under his breath. He had never missed *tefillin* before. His hunger intensified. He chewed a crust of bread from his pocket.

The family reached the front of the line. They placed their bags in front of the gendarme for inspection. He rifled through them roughly, sending items tumbling to the floor. Zushe scrambled to retrieve the velvet bag holding his *tefillin*. The gendarme saw Tzipporah's gold necklace. He grabbed it and stuffed it in his pocket. Tzipporah's eyes widened, but she said nothing. The gendarme finished his search. "Keep moving," he ordered.

A guard gave Shloime a shove. They were hurried onto the platform, where Jews who had already been searched were waiting. Many were in tears, or close to it. Others were praying. The wails of babies were incessant. A long train of wood-paneled cattle cars sat idle on the track. They waited longer. Yankel's mother was shifting from foot to foot. Shivering, she drew her coat closer to her body. Yankel could tell that her strength was fading. He ate a little more food from his pocket. He was so thirsty.

The searches in the station were completed and the platform filled to capacity. Whistles began to blow, followed by cursing and shoves from the guards. The doors of the cattle cars were slid open. Guards began to force Jews in, fifty to eighty people to a car.

The deportees fought to retain hold of their luggage and avoid the blows of clubs as they scrambled aboard. The floors were lined with manure. Feet slick from the mud and snow of Czernowitz's streets slipped on the refuse. Passengers fell to the floor, soiling their clothes as they struggled to rise.

Yankel and his family were shoved onto a car. It quickly

filled to capacity, but the soldiers kept pushing more people on board. Humanity squeezed him on all sides. He couldn't fall even if he wanted to, let alone sit. Two small windows, about one foot by two feet, were situated high up on each side of the car. They were boarded over with slats of wood. The Wiesenfeld-Reiners were relatively lucky. They were crammed against the wall of the car and therefore were not surrounded by people on all sides.

Once the guards had packed in as many people as humanly possible, the doors slid shut. A wail of despair rent the air. He could hear boards of wood being nailed over the doors of the car. The car was pitch black. People standing near the doors began banging on them as hard as they could, yelling helplessly.

With a hiss of steam and the clank of pistons, the train came to life and began slowly to depart. The sound of forty screaming infants was deafening. People began to pray aloud. Many wept openly. Yankel heard his mother mutter Psalms under her breath.

The train crept along at a snail's pace. He could barely breathe. The stuffiness and claustrophobia were overwhelming. Some of the men began hammering the boards covering the windows, striving to knock them loose. Zushe, who was tall, followed suit, and the men eventually succeeded in knocking the boards free. Yankel felt cold air penetrate the car. It brought a tiny measure of relief. People began to fight to stand near the windows. Zushe, who was bigger than most, shoved them away.

The train continued through the night and into the next morning. He knew he should ration his food, but he was too hungry and ate the remainder. There was nothing to drink. The number of crying babies had decreased, but the weeping continued. There were no bathrooms and no empty corners. People relieved themselves on the spot. Empty bowls were used as receptacles for bowel movements. Yankel felt his stomach churn. Several people vomited. The bowls were passed to the men near the windows who reached up and emptied them outside. The wind blew much of it back into the passengers' faces, sending people into hysterics.

Yankel couldn't feel his feet. His thirst grew more acute by the minute. The stench of feces, urine, vomit, and sweat clogged his throat. His mother was still reciting Psalms beside him, her voice growing weaker. He thought back to his boyhood. He had surprised his father once by memorizing *Shir HaShirim,* the Song of Songs. He began to recite it to himself. The lofty prose, a paean to beauty and grace, belied his hellish surroundings.

"I must rise and roam the town, Through the streets and through the squares; I must seek my beloved. I sought but found him not," Yankel intoned. *"I met the watchmen who patrol the town. Have you seen my beloved?"*

His mother continued her prayers beside him. When he finished the poem, he recited it again. Then again, and then a fourth time. When day once again turned to night, he stopped reciting. He no longer heard his mother's prayers. There was not even room for Tzipporah's body to fall to the floor. Yankel heard his father weeping softly. Very few babies were still crying.

The following morning, a woman named Rothkopf lost her mind. She began to rave incoherently, ranting about her parents and siblings, her childhood playing on the banks of the River Prut. She rambled for hours. No one made a move to silence her. He felt that he, too, was slowly going insane from thirst.

After three days and nights, the train ground to a halt.

The passengers strained against the door to be free of the confines of the train as quickly as possible. Agonizing seconds ticked by as the wooden boards were removed. After what seemed an eternity, the doors were flung open. Yankel blinked in the bright sunlight and shielded his eyes. A sign on the platform read, "Atachi".

13

"**O**ut! Out!" Romanian soldiers began cursing and swinging their clubs. The passengers scrambled to disembark, slipping on human and animal waste and tripping over dead bodies. Some of them fell off the car to the ground, too weak to stand; these unfortunates were cruelly beaten.

Yankel and his father and brother quickly climbed down from the car, supporting Tzipporah's body between them. When they hit the ground, a soldier grabbed the brothers and pulled them away. "Leave the body!" he ordered. Shloime refused to let go. The guard struck his face with a closed fist. Shloime staggered, but still held on. The guard raised his truncheon. Yankel and Zushe grabbed their father by each of his arms and hauled him away. Tzipporah's body was left lying on the ground, the book of Psalms still clasped tightly in her hand.

A dirty puddle stood where snow had melted. The brothers fell to their knees and began slurping greedily. They were quickly joined by other passengers. It was the most delicious thing Yankel had ever tasted. The puddle was quickly drained. He looked up. A young woman nearby was attempting to nurse her baby. The baby was dead. Few infants from his car survived the journey.

Guards began yelling orders. "Move! Find shelter and stay there! Anyone caught leaving the settlement will be shot. Leave your belongings behind."

Shloime, his face beginning to swell from the soldier's blow, managed to retrieve the family's identification papers before the group was driven along by soldiers' clubs. Yankel forlornly glanced behind him where their small pile of baggage lay. Their bags contained three sets of *tefillin*, their most precious remaining possessions. Soldiers were already rummaging through the bags, looking for valuables.

Yankel, his father, and his brother stumbled into the town. The sight filled them with despair. It was a tiny settlement, comprising a handful of houses, barns, and stables. It had been totally bombed out in the early days of the invasion. Virtually every structure lacked a door or roof. Not a window remained intact. Thousands of wretched Jews filled the village, crammed into every available nook and cranny. Horrified, Yankel observed half-naked children shivering in the cold. Barefoot people, their feet blackened by frostbite, sat listlessly on the hard ground. Swollen eyes and mouths rendered faces unrecognizable. Women cradled dead and dying children.

Yankel saw Velvel was among the newcomers looking for a place to shelter for the night. He was filthy. He figured that he must look the same. Velvel turned when he heard his name called. He joined the Wiesenfeld-Reiners, his eyes filled with sorrow. Yankel saw that Velvel was alone. He did not need to ask what happened to his mother.

The foursome found a partially-standing stable and entered. People of both sexes and all ages lined the floors. Many protested that there was no room, but Yankel and his family ignored them. They found a relatively clear space and collapsed in exhaustion. The companions huddled together to ward off the freezing night air. Hunger gnawed at Yankel's gut, but he immediately fell into a troubled sleep.

He awoke to the sound of screams. He jerked upright to find three Romanian soldiers among the Jews in the stable. Two of them had two young women by the hair and were dragging them, screaming, into the cold night. One of their male relatives tried to pull a girl away. The third soldier beat him with a rifle butt until the man lay senseless, bleeding profusely. The soldiers left, dragging their captives screaming behind them.

He didn't sleep the rest of the night. Several hours later, one of the girls crawled back to the stable. She was sobbing. Her face was bruised and bloody, and her clothes were in tatters. She curled into a fetal position and began to shake.

The night seemed to last forever. He had never been so cold. Dawn broke, casting a grey pallor over the bedraggled group and illuminating Shloime's face. The sight struck Yankel with fear. His father sat with his back against the wall, staring hollowly into the distance. His will to live seemed to have left him; he looked utterly defeated.

Yankel's hunger pains had grown sharper. Zushe spoke for all of them. "*Tatte*, we need to do something about food. We need our strength."

Shloime looked unseeingly up at his elder son. Then he removed his shoe. He withdrew a battered pocket watch from where he'd hidden it in the sole. Zushe nodded his understanding and left the stable.

Zushe returned sometime later with a loaf of bread. He tore it into four pieces and distributed it to his companions. Yankel tore into his portion ravenously. It was the coarsest bread he'd ever encountered. It appeared to be milled with sand and bran. Still, he consumed his piece in several large bites. Zushe crouched and ate his bread at a more measured pace. For the first time, Yankel saw how much skinnier his strongly built brother had become. His face seemed narrower somehow, his actions slower.

When they had finished, Zushe spoke up again. "The village is on the banks of the Dniester. We should wash ourselves. We aren't animals."

Yankel nodded his agreement. He was anxious about leaving the stable, but he was determined to be as resourceful as Zushe. Shloime didn't react. He just sat there, staring into space.

Zushe looked at his father sadly. "We'll be back soon, *Tatte*." The two brothers and Velvel left the stable and made their way toward the river. Guards were stationed at intervals in a ring around the village, but most of them were chatting with each other or leering at the women. It proved easy enough to slip by and scramble down to the banks of the Dniester.

Yankel stopped in his tracks and his mouth dropped. The river was something out of his worst nightmare. The bloated corpses of humans and horses filled the river, bumping into each other as they floated along. Severed limbs lay everywhere. Torah scrolls and holy books, ripped to shreds, were scattered among the carnage. Yankel could see the body of one man still wrapped in his black and white prayer shawl.

Zushe steeled himself, walked to the water's edge, and removed his coat, shirt, and fringed *tzitzis*. Crouching, he cupped some of the filthy water and began rubbing it on his face, under his arms, along his prominent ribs. Yankel and Velvel reluctantly followed suit. The water was freezing and numbed Yankel's hands, but he did his best to rub the filth of the last few days off of himself.

He started when gunshots rang out and swung around. Further down the river, a mother and young daughter had been spotted by a guard on the way back to the settlement from the river, where they apparently had also been washing. The guard didn't bother to move from where he was leaning against a fence and casually fired at them. The mother and daughter dropped to the ground and began crawling furiously below the flying bullets.

Yankel and his companions looked at each other. Zushe motioned that they should also crawl. Wordlessly, they dressed and began slithering up the embankment, taking care to detour around a shed to avoid the soldier's line of sight. Yankel stifled a gasp when he almost bumped into a female corpse, her eyes open and staring. It was the girl who did not return to the stable last night. Her clothes were torn from her body and she clutched a shard of glass in her right hand. Matted blood clung to her wrist where it had flowed freely from her self-inflicted wound. They kept on crawling.

When they returned to the stable, Shloime was sitting where they'd left him. He looked up briefly when his sons rejoined him, then continued staring in the distance. Most of the occupants of the stable were awake at this point.

The man who was beaten the previous night lay still. Zushe looked at his brother. "We need to bury him." Yankel nodded. He, Velvel, and Zushe grabbed hold of the man and dragged him outside. The effort left Yankel gasping. Using scraps of wood, they dug a shallow grave in the wet mud. They placed the dead man inside and scooped the dirt atop him.

They stood and together recited *Kaddish*, the mourner's prayer, from memory. Yankel closed his eyes and thought of his mother. He also thought of Hirsch and prayed for his safety. His tears flowed freely.

They spent another freezing night in the stable. Yankel was in agony. The coarse bread wreaked havoc on his gut. Judging from the groans of his companions, they suffered similarly.

The next morning, a soldier woke them with a yell. He tossed a bucket of cornmeal into the stable. "Eat quickly!" he barked. "Then line up outside." The occupants of the stable scrambled for their shares of cornmeal. Yankel managed to grab a handful and swallowed it greedily. It was hard and unmilled, but he ate it just the same. Zushe retrieved two handfuls. He offered some to his father, urging him to eat. Shloime silently accepted.

Driven on by the cries and blows of the guards they exited the stable to the road, joining the thousands of Jews doing the same. He could see the forms of many dead bodies left behind in the ramshackle shelters. No burial awaited them. A guard shoved him from behind. "Move it!"

They began walking toward the river. Dozens of barges stood in the water alongside the muddy banks waiting to ferry the refugees across the Dniester. Romanian soldiers were posted along the bank. The nearest one approached Shloime. "Papers," he ordered.

He relayed the instructions to his father. Shloime produced them from inside his coat. The soldier glanced at them. He looked up. "Wiesenfeld-Reiner?" Shloime nodded.

The soldier tore the papers to shreds and tossed them to the ground. "Now you're nobody. Get in the boat."

Yankel and his group approached one of the barges, manned by a large Ukrainian, wielding a long pole. Zushe moved to step aboard the boat, but the man blocked him. "Pay me," he said.

Zushe looked at Yankel quizzically. "He wants payment," he told Zushe. Zushe turned back to the man and spread his hands. "We have no money," said Yankel in Ukrainian.

The man smiled widely; he was missing several teeth. He pointed at Zushe's coat. "He's my size," the man said.

Zushe looked at Yankel again. "He wants your coat." Yankel turned to the bargeman. "You don't want that coat. It's filthy." Indeed, after days of hellish conditions and exposure to the elements, Zushe's coat was ragged and crusted in mud.

The bargeman was still smiling. He gestured toward a soldier stationed a dozen yards down the riverbank. The soldier was peering at Zushe suspiciously, his rifle held loosely before him. Zushe looked back at the smiling bargeman. The bargeman spoke in a matter-of-fact tone. "Give me the coat or stay here and die."

Zushe understood. Wordlessly, his jaw clenched, Zushe peeled off his coat and handed it to the bargeman. The man stepped aside and allowed him to board. Yankel attempted to follow, but the man blocked him as well. "Yours too."

Yankel looked up in surprise. He then resignedly handed his coat over and joined his brother on the barge. Smiling wickedly, the bargeman subjected Shloime and Velvel to the same treatment. When all four coats were in hand, the man tossed the lot into the river with a satisfied smile.

Yankel and his companions huddled miserably in the cold as the barge filled with more Jews. No Jew was allowed to board the boat without some form of payment. Several Romanian soldiers boarded as well.

Yankel saw the bargeman rip the earrings from the ears of one woman. She resisted, begging him to allow her to keep them. With one meaty hand, the bargeman grabbed her by the coat and flung her into the water. She thrashed about in a panic. A man hurried to the water and reached a hand to the woman. A Romanian soldier shot them both. The lifeless bodies floated away, trailing a stream of blood.

When the boat was crammed full of Jews, the bargeman pushed off and began steering across the Dniester. The river soon filled with barges carrying miserable Jews to an unknown destination. Yankel heard a soldier from a neighboring boat call to his friend.

"Let's see if these Jews can part the Red Sea!" The soldier gleefully hauled an elderly man off his feet and hurled him into the river. His friend on another barge laughed and grabbed a child from his mother. The mother flung herself at the soldier and began clawing at him frantically. The soldier tossed the boy over the side and then grabbed the mother and did the same.

The soldiers on Yankel's barge chuckled appreciatively

but made no move towards any passenger. He could see three heads struggling to remain above the water. One by one, they disappeared beneath the current.

The barge ground to a halt at the far bank. They had reached Transnistria.

14

There was a large town on the far side of the river. It was called Moghilev. Before the war, twenty thousand Jews had resided there, comprising twenty percent of the town's population. Most of them were now dead, slain by the *Einsatzgruppen,* deported to death camps deep in Transnistria or carried away by hunger and disease. Moghilev was still occupied by twenty thousand Jews. Most of these were newcomers, stateless exiles from Bukovina, Bessarabia, and Transylvania. They were confined to a tiny ghetto in the Jewish part of town. This is where Yankel and his fellow prisoners were taken.

Much like Atachi, Moghilev was heavily bombed during the German invasion. Most houses lacked windows, doors, and roofs. Every structure, no matter how unsound, was filled to capacity. Forty, fifty people were crammed into tiny houses. Filthy, disheveled men and women lined the floors of decrepit stables and pigsties. Many people were naked. They walked the streets of Moghilev, their protruding ribs and hipbones exposed to the cold Ukrainian air. Their clothes had rotted right off their bodies, the consequence of months of lice and filth.

A group of Jewish men passed by the convoy, escorted by Ukrainian police officers. They carried shovels, picks and buckets, yellow stars prominent on their clothing. They plodded along, stooped with exhaustion. The very act of dragging their feet seemed to cost them dearly. Several pairs of men carried stretchers between them. The stretchers bore corpses, their arms dangling off the side and trailing in the dirt.

Yankel was struck by the silence. He heard no cries, no wails, no groans. The inhabitants of Moghilev trudged in deadly silence. If they didn't walk, they sat or lay down. They leaned on structures every chance they could. They appeared to be saving every ounce of energy to remain alive.

The convoy was marched to an open field alongside the ghetto. A crude gallows stood there. Eight wretched Jews hung by their necks, their heads bent at grotesque angles. A wagon filled with shovels was parked beside the dead men. The pit of dread in his stomach hardened.

They were ordered to line up for inspection. Policemen walked among the Jews, looking each one up and down. The policemen began to seize old men and women, the weak and the injured. Those selected were herded to the side and grouped together. One young man protested as his father was grabbed by a Ukrainian policeman. The policeman balled his fist and struck the young man in the gut. The young Jew doubled over as his father was led away.

Some of the newcomers drew money and valuables hidden away in their clothing as policemen approached. Those who managed to smuggle money this far tried to bribe their captors. Those successful at doing so were sent scurrying to the ghetto to try and find housing of some kind. Yankel and Zushe looked at each other balefully. They had nothing but the clothes on their backs.

Zushe was visibly nervous. Shloime had not emerged from the stupor induced by his wife's death during the trip in the cattle car. Shloime stood slack, his shoulders slumped. His face had begun to adopt a grey pallor. Zushe glanced around to make sure no policemen were watching. He reached up and vigorously patted his father's cheeks to restore some color. Zushe pulled his father's shoulders back to prop him up as best he could.

"*Tatte*," Zushe whispered urgently. "You must try to look strong."

Shloime didn't seem to hear his son.

The policeman drew closer. Yankel's pulse quickened. He drew himself up to his full height. He was young, but he'd never felt so weak. He was faint from hunger, and the deep cold had set into his bones. He knew he didn't look as strong as Zushe, or even Velvel. He clenched his jaw and said a silent prayer.

The policeman drew near to Velvel. Velvel's eyes were shut tight. The policeman looked him over and moved on. It was Yankel's turn. He held his breath. The policeman barely registered his presence and moved on to Zushe. Zushe received the same treatment as Yankel. The policeman hesitated for a few seconds when he reached Shloime. Shloime looked through the policeman, his expression blank. The policeman moved on.

Yankel slowly exhaled.

They remained standing in this fashion for the remainder of the day. When dusk came, dozens of old and sick people stood huddled in a group near the gallows. A line of policemen approached, rifles cocked. The sergeant barked an order and the air filled with the sound of discharging weapons. When the execution was complete, the sergeant opened the wagon carrying the shovels, spilling many to the hard ground.

"Get digging," he ordered.

They camped in the field that night, bereft of food or shelter. The four companions huddled for warmth. Yankel, exhausted from hours of burying the dead, struggled to fall asleep despite the deep hunger wracking his frame. He had never been so cold.

The process was repeated the following day. Many had been weakened by the lack of food and a night out in the elements, enabling the policemen to separate another set of victims. Shloime, although he seemed to weaken by the hour, was again not selected. Dusk came, and the chosen were summarily executed. The dead were buried, and the survivors collapsed in exhaustion as soon as permitted. He saw a man tear grass from the ground and eat it. He grasped a few blades and pulled. Even that small gesture took an effort. He placed them in his mouth and chewed. He was glad for the nourishment. It rained that night.

He wasn't sure he could stand the next morning, but he dragged himself to his feet. He was gratified to see his father do likewise. The selections continued. Shloime seemed to sway on his feet, his eyes half closed. Once again, the four companions were not chosen for execution. When dusk came, they buried the dead.

The sergeant took his place at the front of the killing grounds. "Tomorrow, we head out," he boomed.

They slept in the field once more. Yells and kicks woke them up the next morning. His eyes felt frozen shut. His chest ached with cold. The hunger was unbearable. He rose to his feet. Zushe helped Shloime stand. The grey in Shloime's face had deepened. Many remained unmoving where they lay.

They were ordered to march west at a brisk pace. The weak could not keep up. Stragglers were shot. Zushe kept a tight grip on his father's arm.

People were starving. Some of them begged the guards for food. The guards laughed and shoved them back in the procession. Sometimes the beggars were shot. Young women offered their bodies to the soldiers in exchange for a crust of bread. The soldiers happily accepted the offer, dragging the women off to the side of the road. They often did not provide the promised crusts. Some of these women asked the guards to kill them. The guards readily complied.

The hunger was indescribable. His body screamed for nourishment. A group of Ukrainian peasant women passed them on the road, carrying their market produce. When they saw the state of the captives, they began to weep. Several begged the guards to let them distribute food. Others didn't wait for permission and started tossing provisions into the procession. Furious fights broke out as starving people hurled themselves toward the food, snarling, scratching, and kicking. Humanity was forgotten in the face of brutal hunger.

He scrabbled in the mud, desperate for food. He rose with an apple in one hand and a hunk of bread in the other. He began to chew ravenously. He saw Zushe share some of his own bread with Shloime. Shamefacedly, Yankel turned to Velvel and offered some of his food. Velvel accepted gratefully. Shloime barely had the strength to swallow.

They reached swampland. Yankel struggled to walk as

he sank ankle-deep in the mud. Shloime clung to his sons as they gingerly navigated the road, seeking a relatively firm path. Many of their companions weren't so lucky and were sucked into the mire. The procession was forced onward, the rising muck ultimately silencing the screams of the doomed.

By day's end, they reached the village of Lucinetz.

15

Lucinetz was a tiny Transnistrian village that housed one hundred and fifty families before the war, fifty of whom were Jewish. Many of those Jews were now dead. A barbed wire fence was erected around the Jewish part of town, guarded by German soldiers. Lucinetz became a dumping ground for Jewish exiles to die from hunger, disease, violence, and exposure.

The surviving members of the convoy were herded towards the ghetto. They passed by a long narrow ditch filled with mud and debris. Yankel heard Velvel's sharp intake of breath and turned to look at the ditch more closely. The debris was, in fact, a jumble of corpses and body parts.

The wretched group was marched through an opening in the barbed wire and into the ghetto proper. At this point, Zushe was practically dragging his father. Dirty, sunken faces peered at the newcomers from behind the doors of tiny clay houses. A horse drawn sledge, laden with more dead bodies, passed the procession. The air seemed to grow colder with every passing moment.

They reached a large storehouse, devoid of doors or windows, in the center of town. The nearest guard gave Velvel a shove that sent him staggering. "Inside," the guard ordered. They entered the storehouse.

The stench was terrible. Hundreds of Jews – men, women, and children – lay on the floor, human waste mixing with the straw. The occupants of the storehouse were in a pitiable condition. Many lacked shoes and clothing. Some of the occupants lay totally still. Hacking coughs resounded from every corner of the room. One small boy approached him. The boy was filthy, and his head appeared to be shaved. He wore nothing but a ragged shirt. Yankel could see a swollen stomach protruding from an otherwise gaunt frame. *"Essen?"* he asked quietly in Yiddish. Food?

Tears sprang unbidden to his eyes. He shook his head.

The boy slumped away, dejected.

The occupants of the storehouse were not happy about having to make room for more people. Yankel and his companions found a small spot on the straw to lie down. Zushe helped Shloime, his strength greatly diminished, lower himself to the floor. They were lucky. Many in their convoy were forced to sleep under an open sky or seek refuge in pigsties and stables. Once again, the four men huddled together for warmth and closed their eyes.

They were roused at dawn the next morning by the hollers of the soldiers, who banged their truncheons against the open door frame. "Roll call!" a soldier barked. "Report to the town square for work detail!"

Yankel slowly opened his eyes. His teeth chattered violently, and the hunger pangs had intensified. His legs were sore from the long march from Moghilev. His body itched. He scratched at his shoulder. He felt something skitter across his hand. It were lice. He glanced at the floor. The straw was crawling with lice. He barely had the strength to feel revolted. Yankel slowly hauled himself to his feet.

Zushe was crouched next to their father, shaking him urgently. "*Tatte*, we need to get up," he whispered. He was alarmed to hear a note of panic in his normally stoic brother's voice. Shloime's eyes fluttered. He lay on the ground listlessly.

Zushe looked up at Yankel anxiously. "He can't work," he whispered. "We need to hide him." Zushe cast about desperately. The other occupants of the storehouse were slowly rising to their feet and shambling towards the exit. Zushe locked eyes with a stooped man limping by. The man looked about fifty. He was probably thirty-five.

"Please," Zushe implored, "is there anywhere we can hide him?"

The man considered Zushe hollowly. "Leave him. They'll collect him on the sledge with the rest." The man limped away. Yankel was feeling desperate. He knew Zushe felt the same. Time was running out.

He felt a bony hand grasp his arm. He spun around. An older woman in a kerchief was standing there. She gestured towards the far corner of the room. "The cellar," she whispered.

His eyes widened. "There's a cellar?"

The old woman put her finger to her lips and nodded. Then she walked away.

Yankel grabbed hold of one of his father's arms and gestured for Zushe and Velvel to follow suit. "Come on," he urged.

They struggled to carry Shloime's weight to the area indicated by the old woman. They saw nothing but floorboards. Yankel kicked the wood with his foot. It sounded hollow. He and Zushe pulled at one of the boards. There were no nails holding it in place and it came away cleanly. A second board alongside the first was similarly unattached. They lifted it away and peered inside.

Several sickly people were hidden there. Apparently, someone had ripped out the floorboards in preparation for such an instance. They glared angrily at the brothers, fearful of discovery. "Get him inside, quick!" a man hissed when he saw Shloime's limp frame. The three friends lowered him to the dirt floor as quickly and gently as they could. Shloime lay there in the dark, breathing shallowly. Yankel gave his father one more look and replaced the boards, plunging the cellar into darkness.

The storehouse was almost empty save for a few stragglers and the people who never awoke from the previous night's slumber. Yankel noticed the starving boy from the previous day was among the dead. Yankel and his companions hurried to catch up with the rest of the prisoners.

The Jewish prisoners were lined up in the square. The square contained a freezing well, where the prisoners hurried to wash themselves before they stood at attention for work. He quickly took his place alongside Zushe and Velvel. They had no time to use the well, delayed as they were by their father's condition. Gendarmes counted the assembled Jews. Others prowled through the ranks, truncheons in hand. Occasionally, they grabbed a prisoner at random and pulled him from the ranks to beat him. If the worker was able to stand after the beating he would rejoin the labor gang. Otherwise, the gendarmes left him where he lay. He stood there and prayed he wouldn't be chosen. He also prayed the guards would give them something to eat. The beatings eventually stopped. No food was provided.

The prisoners were marched several kilometers to a worksite outside of the camp. They were assigned to work in a quarry. Large chunks of rocks were dynamited into smaller chunks. Workers with sledgehammers broke these chunks down even further, which were then loaded into wheelbarrows. His job was to push the wheelbarrow up the steep incline of the quarry to where the women waited to load the contents into waiting trucks.

The work was crushing. Blisters formed on his hands almost immediately. He felt his body would crumple under the strain, but he dared not rest. Workers collapsed all around him. The lucky ones were shot. Otherwise they were beaten to death. Yankel watched a man pummeled to a pulp in front of his young son. The man did not get up after the beating, and his son had no choice but to keep working. The boy cried to himself as he continued his labor. He couldn't have been older than thirteen or fourteen. He thought of Hirsch.

At noon, four prisoners arrived pushing two wheelbarrows full of water. The work brigade was allowed to stop and drink. Yankel slurped the water greedily. He'd drunk nothing but rainwater since leaving Czernowitz. His thirst quenched, his body screamed for sustenance. He knew he wouldn't last the day if he didn't eat.

As if on cue, the man next to him at the barrow nudged him. He pulled his coat aside and revealed a small satchel. The contents of the satchel, several turnips and a half a loaf of course bread, sent a pang of hunger through his gut. "Want food?" the man whispered. Yankel nodded vigorously and reached for a turnip. The man slapped his hand away. He pointed at Yankel's feet. "Give me your shoes," the man ordered.

He looked at his feet in surprise. His shoes were battered almost beyond recognition from weeks of abuse. They were crusted with mud and a hole was forming near the toes of his right foot. He knew he needed shoes, but he was desperate. He quickly removed them and handed them over. Yankel almost cried with joy when the man slipped him the turnips and bread.

He worked his way over to Zushe and Velvel, exhausted and dusty from breaking rocks, to share his findings. They accepted gratefully, although Zushe looked saddened when he saw his stocking feet. Zushe placed a portion of his food in his pocket.

"We need to save some for *Tatte*," he told Yankel. With a massive effort, Yankel forced himself to stop eating. He too slipped the remainder of the food in his pocket. The order came to return to work. He walked painfully back to his wheelbarrow.

The remainder of the day was agony. The food gave Yankel some strength, but the rough ground cut into his feet. He was careful not to drop any stones on his unprotected insteps. His stockings were shredded, and his soles bled freely. He dared not tend to the wounds. Yankel's discomfort was compounded by worry for his father, nearing starvation in a dark cellar, surrounded by strangers. He feared Shloime would not survive the day.

They worked until eight in the evening when the labor was halted, and marched back to Lucinetz in neat lines. The prisoners, spent from the mental and physical strain of the day, marched in silence. His bare feet were on fire with pain They brought the corpses along – evening roll

call was required to match the morning's count. Velvel was
assigned to carry a stretcher and labored under the dead
weight.. They passed a group of Jews on the road who
were crouching over a dead horse and eating its flesh. His
stomach rumbled.

They returned to the square in the ghetto and once
again were assembled. The morning's ritual was repeated,
complete with the beatings. When the gendarmes had
their fill of violence, the prisoners were allowed to return
to the storehouse. Yankel, Zushe, and Velvel hurried back
as fast as their sore bodies would carry them.

Shloime was still alive. They lifted him from the hole
in the ground and laid him on the straw. His breathing
had grown shallower and his face greyer, a sheen of sweat
covered his brow. Zushe slowly tried to feed Shloime bits
of the bread he'd saved. He could not coax his catatonic
father to chew. Zushe had managed to soak a strip of cloth
from his shirt in the well. He dripped some water through
Shloime's parched lips.

Yankel and Zushe sat vigil over their father that night.
Yankel occasionally slipped into a doze, only to snap back
to consciousness in a panic and check on his father in a
panic. In the wee hours of the morning, he drifted off.

Zushe shook him awake near dawn. Yankel opened his
eyes with a start. His brother's drawn face said everything.
He and Zushe sat by their father's cold body and whispered psalms from memory. The streets were patrolled by
guards at this time of night. It was too risky to attempt a
burial. Dawn came and the guards arrived to return the
sleeping prisoners to their hellish reality. The brothers
had no choice but to leave Shloime's body where it lay
and report to the square for work detail.

He barely felt the pain in his feet and the hunger in his

belly at the quarry that day. He was bent over with sorrow. His family had been torn from his life one by one. He realized that he could be next.

When he and Zushe returned to the storehouse that night, Shloime's body was gone.

belly aching that day. He was bent over with cramps.
His family had been torn from his life one by one. No one
told him he could bear it.

When he and Zushe returned to the bunkhouse that
night, Shloime had, as Zushe...

16

Life in the Lucinetz ghetto was miserable. He woke every morning to the screams and blows of the guards. He would hustle to the town square and try to arrive with enough time to quickly splash his face with cold well water before he lined up for roll call. Then he was marched to work in the quarry to break and haul stones for twelve hours.

Sometimes the workers were fed. More often they were not. When there was food, they were usually given potato peels. Sometimes they were lucky and received coarse bread or watery pea soup. The soup wreaked havoc on shrunken bellies. Many died from the after effects. When Yankel was fortunate enough to obtain bread, he forced himself to make it last as long as he could. He'd eat half and sleep that night with the other half clutched tightly under his body so no one could steal it. He felt his body breaking down from the strain. Zushe, too, was affected by the adverse conditions. He was alarmed to see his tall brother turn into a walking skeleton clad in rags.

Yankel's feet grew tough and calloused from the rough ground. The weather grew more frigid and he knew he would soon need shoes to protect him from cold in addition to the rocks. Zushe and Velvel had long since traded their shoes for food as well.

He grew used to being struck. The guards were quick to show their displeasure, using clubs, boots, and rifle butts. Each day was an endless parade of blows. The unlucky ones were hauled off the work line and subjected to twenty-five lashes. Many did not survive. Those who resisted were shot.

Death was constant. Every day the horse-drawn sledge came by the storehouse to collect those who had not survived the previous night. Five to twelve bodies were removed at a time. Every evening, the work detail was forced to carry their dead back to the ghetto for roll call. He grew so used to the sight of people collapsing from hunger that he barely noticed it.

Several thousand Jews were penned in the ghetto, crammed into houses, sheds, stables and the storehouse. To some degree, they managed to organize themselves. A *hevra kadisha,* a burial society, operated with the consent of the Romanian authorities. They were the ones who collected the bodies on the sledge. There was also an orphanage, which consisted of little more than starving, naked children shivering under ragged blankets, six or seven to a bed. People that were caught bringing food to the orphanage were often severely beaten or killed.

The temperature in Lucinetz was freezing. At night, the temperature regularly dropped well below zero. Shoes were the exception rather than the norm, and frostbite was rampant. The inmates, most lacking coats and many lacking proper shirts, regularly froze to death. For Yankel, bone-deep cold became a fact of life.

The dead grew so numerous, the *hevra kadisha* grew overwhelmed. Sometimes bodies lay in the street or in the storehouse for a week or more before they were buried. Sometimes they were not buried at all. Corpses left in the street were eventually ravaged by scavenger dogs.

His entire existence attained a singular focus – survival. Every ounce of energy he had was spent struggling to attain that goal. Personalities disappeared in the ghetto; that was a luxury the prisoners could not afford. Everyone had the same affect – silent, fearful, hollow eyes trained at the floor. Yankel's daily existence became a struggle to stay alive from minute to minute, day to day. He learned not to upset the guards, to move carefully in his work so as to not drop anything. He learned to conserve his energy. He never walked when he could stand; never stood when he could lean; never leaned when he could sit; never sat when he could lie down. Small efforts took a massive amount of energy. The simple task of pulling a bucket of water from a well left him gasping for air.

Yankel's disintegrating clothes swarmed with lice. There was nothing he could do about the pests, so he ignored them. He was in good company. Every prisoner was lice-infested. There were no bathrooms or privies. Living conditions were abhorrent. Men relieved themselves in front of women, and vice versa. Shame was a memory from a different life.

The work at the quarry completed, Yankel, Zushe, and Velvel were reassigned to the railroad work brigade. They laid railroad tracks and hauled debris. The new work was not much better than the quarry. If they were lucky, some of the Ukrainian laborers would throw them scraps of food. The starving Jewish inmates would fall on the meager offerings and fight over them like a pack of dogs. He grew accustomed to eating handfuls of dirt and grass in order to get through the day. He feared his efforts were futile but nevertheless stubbornly clung to life.

17

W eak from hunger, Yankel staggered under the weight of a rock he was clearing from the rail path. The heavy rock slipped from his grasp and hit the lip of a wheelbarrow with a loud clang, tipping the barrow over and upsetting its contents. Yankel froze. Zushe looked up in horror. Yankel scrambled to right the barrow and refill it as a gendarme walked over. There was something threatening in his gaze. The guard gave Yankel a long hard look, then walked away.

Yankel spent the rest of the day in a state of high anxiety. He seemed to have escaped terrible punishment, but something about the way the guard looked at him told him otherwise. That evening, he stood in the square for roll call. The gendarmes made their usual rounds of the prisoners. The gendarme from earlier, the one who had approached when he had upset the wheelbarrow, was among them. He saw Yankel and, beckoning another guard over, began to thread his way through the assembled laborers. His blood turned to ice. The gendarmes reached him. With gloved hands they each grabbed one of his arms in iron grips.

"No!" Zushe gasped.

There was no resisting. In his weakened state, he was pulled along effortlessly to the front of the square. One of the guards gave him a shove that sent him stumbling. The guard from the work detail swung his truncheon.

The blow sent him crashing to the ground. He saw stars. The guard hit him again. He tasted blood. The blows continued. Yankel heard screams. He detachedly realized they were his own. The guard eventually tired of striking and walked away. He was left on the ground, barely conscious, broken and bleeding. When the prisoners were dismissed, Zushe and Velvel grabbed him by his underarms and dragged him back to the storehouse.

He spent the night drifting in and out of consciousness. His body was on fire. He was only vaguely aware of Zushe's presence next to him. One of the prisoners used to be a doctor. He helped Zushe clean his brother's wounds with a wet rag. There was no medicine. There was nothing to do but wait.

The next morning. Zushe hid him in the cellar. He lay in the dark, breathing the musty air, barely aware of his surroundings. At one point he briefly woke to see one of the other men hiding in the cellar staring at him.

The man looked concerned. "Can you hear me?" the man whispered. "It's time to say *Viduy*." The man began to recite the deathbed confession, coaxing Yankel into saying it with him. "*Ashamnu*," he croaked, "*Bagadnu, gazalnu, dibarnu dofi*." We have sinned, we have been treacherous, we have robbed, we have spoken slander. He slipped back into unconsciousness.

He remained hidden in the cellar for a week. Zushe

and Velvel did their best to bring back some food to feed him. For the first few days, he hovered between life and death. As soon as he could stand, Zushe insisted he return to work. It was too risky to hide in the cellar any longer.

On the eighth day, he reported for roll call. It hurt to stand, to walk, to breathe, and his bruises remained prominent on his face. He nevertheless marched to the railroad with the rest of his brigade. Zushe strove to remain by his side as much as he could. Yankel noticed Zushe's belt was gone. His pants were now held up with a length of string. Yankel realized he'd traded it for food to sustain him while he lay wounded in the cellar.

The first day was horribly painful. He was sure he'd collapse, but he made it through, and each successive day was a little easier than the last. On several occasions, he saw the gendarme who'd beaten him. The gendarme didn't seem to remember him at all.

18

One evening Yankel sat in the storehouse after a day on the railroad. It was freezing, and they had been forced to march home through flurrying snow. His feet were beginning to redden from the cold, his toenails starting to blacken. Zushe was already asleep, his feet outstretched, ankle bones protruding alarmingly. Yankel drew some straw around him in an attempt to ward off the cold. He wanted to curl up and close his eyes. He wasn't sure he ever wanted to reopen them.

"Yankel?" Velvel was sitting on the floor next to him, a sad look in his eyes.

With an effort, he turned his head towards his old friend. Velvel looked defeated. "Remember that man in Atachi? The one we buried behind the stable?"

He did remember. It seemed a thousand years ago. His father had still been alive. He nodded.

"When I die, will you make sure I have a Jewish burial? I don't want to lie in the streets for the dogs."

For a few moments, Yankel was silent. Then he

replied. "Velvel," he said slowly. "I'm not strong. I think I'm going to die before you."

Velvel stared at his friend, his eyes burning. "Promise me."

He sighed. "I promise."

Velvel smiled. He rolled onto his side and went to sleep.

19

Yankel was awakened, as he was every morning, to the shouts and clamor of the guards. He painfully rose to his feet. Each morning, standing seemed more difficult than the previous day. Hunger, his constant companion, wracked his body and clouded his thinking.

He heard a groan and turned to Velvel. His friend was standing beside him, his face ashen. *"Essen,"* Velvel said simply. He was swaying on his feet. *"Essen,"* he said again. Then Velvel keeled over and died.

Yankel did not report to roll call that day, despite Zushe's protests. Velvel's was not the only body lying on the floor of the storehouse that morning, and Yankel needed to make certain the *hevra kadisha* did not disregard his friend. Yankel hid in the cellar with the sick. He sat on the floor, arms around his knees, and waited for the sound of the sledge arriving to collect the bodies. He waited all day, but the storehouse was silent.

When the work parties returned to the storehouse, an exhausted Zushe among them, Yankel emerged from the cellar. His body lay where it had fallen. Yankel departed from the storehouse and walked to the Jewish cemetery down the ghetto's tiny main road. The cemetery was surrounded by a low wrought-iron fence. Bodies lay in heaps among the tombstones. A Jew leaned against the gate, observing the dead dispiritedly. He knew his name was Shmiel and that he headed the *hevra kadisha*. Shmiel was weary from constant work.

"Shmiel," he called out.

Shmiel turned to him.

"My friend died in the storehouse. He needs to be buried."

Shmiel shook his head sadly. He spread his hands. "I'm sorry. There's just no room."

"Please," Yankel said. "I promised him." He realized he was crying. "Please," he said again.

Shmiel looked tired and sighed. "Take my wheelbarrow. If you want to bury your friend, you can. Just don't do it here. The cemetery has no more room." He reached into his pocket and proffered a small book of matches. "You'll need this."

He wheeled the barrow back to the storehouse. With Zushe's help, he loaded Velvel's body and wheeled it to the edge of the ghetto. The brothers gathered kindling and built a small fire to soften the ground rendered rock-hard from the Ukrainian cold. They then dug a small grave with their hands and gently lowered Velvel into the ground. They covered the body. Together, they once again recited the *Kaddish* prayer.

As they returned to the storehouse in the Ukrainian night, Yankel made a promise to himself in his friend's memory. Whenever possible, he would do his best to bury the dead.

20

He knew that if he didn't find a way to supplement his diet he would go the way of his father and Velvel and die of starvation. The occasional potato peel and bowl of watery soup was not enough to sustain anyone, let alone a slave subjected daily to backbreaking labor. His young body was breaking down.

He had heard whispers around the storeroom of people slipping out of the ghetto to find work and food. The rumors didn't altogether surprise him. The guards were undisciplined, and with a little forethought, it didn't seem too difficult to slip past them. He convinced Zushe that they should give it a try.

They crept out of the storehouse shortly before dawn, figuring that this was when the guards would be the most tired and lax. Their gambit paid off; there was no guard to be seen, likely to be sleeping off last night's bout of drinking in the local tavern. The brothers quickly made their way to a weak point in the barbed wire. Zushe lifted the bottom of the fence about six inches off the ground.

His heart beating wildly, Yankel slithered underneath. He held the wire for his brother on the other side, allowing Zushe to wriggle through. Zushe quickly rose to his feet and the brothers took off at a run for the woods, the early morning frost crunching beneath their bare feet.

Once they reached the safety of the dense trees, they wandered until they hit a dirt road. They stayed close to the trees to remain hidden, keeping the road in sight. When the sun rose over the sky, they came across a small farm. A woman was moving about, framed by a small house with a thatched roof. She was lifting cords of wood from a stack with difficulty.

The brothers approached gingerly. They didn't want to alarm the woman with their haggard appearance. More importantly, they didn't want her to report them to the authorities. The woman looked around when she heard footsteps approaching. She did not seem the least bit surprised.

Yankel spoke up. "Excuse me," he said in Ukrainian. "We can help you with that in exchange for a bite to eat."

The woman nodded her agreement.

He stepped forward and relieved the woman of the wood. Zushe retrieved another stack from the woodpile. They followed her inside, not daring to believe their good fortune.

The one-room house was little more than a shack, and in ill-repair. It emitted a musky smell. But it was neat, and along the wall he could see a bed. A real bed, with a real pillow. Two small children stood near the bed, staring at the brothers shyly.

Zushe got busy building a fire. When he'd completed the task, the woman placed a pot of rice over the fire. The smell of the boiling rice soon pervaded the room. Yankel's stomach clenched with hunger. It seemed to him that no rice had ever taken so long to cook.

When the rice was finally ready, the woman placed the pot on the floor. She handed a spoon to each of her children and to the brothers. They crouched around the rice in a circle and began to eat.

He almost cried tears of gratitude. He thought he'd never tasted anything as heavenly as that bowl of rice. A battle raged internally as he commanded himself not to wolf the rice down. The battle was quickly lost. His hostess didn't seem to mind. They finished eating.

The woman spoke. "I'm sorry there's no milk," she said. "We had to slaughter the cow for food."

The thought of milk made his head spin. He recalled the milk Uncle Berel used to deliver from the farm. The woman explained that her husband was away fighting in the war, and there was no one to help on the farm. Would they be willing to stay and help for the day? The brothers nodded vigorously. Yankel felt he owed this woman his life. He would have agreed to anything.

The woman set the brothers to work. It was winter, and there was no farm work to be done, but the brothers chopped wood, hauled water from the well, and did repairs around the house. They paused for lunch to share a bowl of *mamaliga,* a porridge made from cornmeal. He ate till he felt his stomach would burst.

At day's end, they walked back to Lucinetz. They slipped under the barbed wire just after roll call before the night guards took their positions. Yankel felt the least hungry he'd been since his exile from Czernowitz. He uttered a silent prayer of thanks as he fell asleep.

From then on, they slipped out of the ghetto to the countryside every few days. Work on the railroad grew more sporadic, and the work brigades sometimes weren't assembled. On these days it was easier to slip away, as the brothers wouldn't risk being missed by a keen-eyed gendarme.

The brothers wandered the countryside, trudging through the snow in their bare feet, offering their services to local peasants in exchange for food. Occasionally, they stayed overnight, sleeping among the livestock to keep warm. With all the men gone to war, many of the Ukrainian women were happy to accept the help and shared their meager rations with the two young men. Once, seeing his bare and frostbitten feet, a woman they assisted reached into a chest and removed an old pair of shoes. They were her son's, she explained, but he was killed fighting the Germans. Yankel could barely stammer his thanks when she handed them to him. They were a little big, but they looked reasonably well made. He rubbed them in the mud so they'd be less conspicuous back in the ghetto.

The brothers would stay in the ghetto for a few days and when they felt their hunger sharpen, they would slip the guards, crawl under the fence, and look for work. The food they received during these sojourns held them over for a while until they were compelled to sneak out once again.

Sometimes, the brothers were joined by Hermann, a secular young man from Iasi. Hermann had caught the two slipping out one morning and insisted they take him along. Fearing exposure, the brothers acquiesced. They were soon glad for his company. He was highly intelligent and resourceful and was unafraid of hard work. Hermann wore round spectacles, which had somehow survived the journey to the Transnistrian hell. The spectacles lent Hermann an intellectual air.

The Romanian authorities were aware that Jews wandered the countryside begging for food, and they sometimes sent out patrols with dogs trained to hunt them down. Jews caught outside the ghetto were immediately shot. the brothers occasionally came across the bodies of these unfortunates. After checking them for food, they always made an effort to bury the corpses.

As the days lengthened and the winter thawed, there was more work to be had. The snow grew less frequent. Yankel returned to the home of the peasant woman who had gifted him shoes. He asked her to hide them. He could make do barefoot in the warm months. He knew that if he survived until next winter, he'd need their protection again. He didn't want to risk wearing them out or losing them to a ghetto thief. The woman agreed to safeguard the shoes. Yankel was grateful.

Yankel crawled under the barbed wire fence one morning in the autumn of 1942 along with Zushe and Hermann as snow began to fall. He was desperate for work. He had not eaten in two days. Weak from hunger, his head pounded from the effort of movement. Yankel and his companions tread quickly through the snow until they'd reached the woods and slowed to a walk.

They'd barely traveled a kilometer when they heard a sound that struck them dumb with terror. A dog was barking not too far behind them. Another dog joined in, and the three companions could hear the sound of gendarmes shouting. The hounds had picked up a trail. The patrol could not have been more than half a kilometer behind them.

Without a word, the three men took off running. They breathed in ragged gasps of mist as they sprinted as fast as their weakened bodies could carry them. The snow fell more heavily, covering their tracks as they ran. The snow was painfully cold against his bare feet, but he paid it no heed as he fought to put distance between himself and his pursuers.

Panic gave them wings, and they ran for what felt like miles. The sounds of the pursuing patrol only seemed to grow closer. When they could run no farther they skidded to a halt, snow swirling around them. He doubled over and gulped air. Breathing heavily, Zushe cast about. His eyes settled on a beech tree with branches low to the ground. He pointed. "Up there! Let's go!"

Fuelled by fear, the three of them clambered up the tree, branch by branch. They kept climbing until the branches could barely hold their weight. The three fugitives clung to the trunk and waited with bated breath.

Thirty feet below their arboreal hiding place, the patrol came into view. Six Romanian gendarmes, accompanied by two hounds, came to a halt beneath the beech and struggled to see through the heavy snowfall. The hounds, sensing their prey was near, circled excitedly. Yankel hoped the snow was sufficient to hide their footprints.

The snow slowed to a flurry. He could make out the gendarmes conversing. They were glancing around, peering behind trunks and up into the trees. The heavily coniferous Ukrainian forest provided some cover even during the winter months. Yankel nevertheless shrunk himself down as small as he could.

One of the gendarmes reached into his rucksack and removed something small and brown. The gendarme held it aloft. He squinted hard. It was a potato. He felt a sharp pang deep in his abdomen.

"Hungry, Jew?" the gendarme called out. He dropped the potato to the ground. It made an indentation in the snow as it sunk beneath the surface. The patrol began to slowly move away. The gendarme reached into his ruck-sack and dropped another potato in the snow. He continued to back away and repeated this process every few feet. Eventually, the patrol disappeared from view, leaving a trail of potatoes behind them.

Yankel felt weak. The terror-fuelled run through the forest had only served to starve his body of its little remaining resources. The potatoes were so close. All he had to do was slip down to the ground, grab one, and climb back up. The Romanians would be none the wiser.

Zushe seemed to read his thoughts. "Don't take the bait," he whispered. Yankel shook his head to clear his mind of hunger-induced cobwebs. His brother was right. To retrieve a potato was suicide. The gendarmes would tire of the game eventually. They'd wait the patrol out.

Hours passed. He couldn't feel his arms clinging to the tree trunk. His headache returned with a vengeance. He could barely see. He feared he would soon lose his strength and plummet thirty feet to the snowy ground below.

Yankel gazed at the snow. He could still make out the indentation where the gendarme had dropped the first potato. It was so close. He could almost taste it. The craving was overpowering. He shifted in the tree. Zushe placed a warning hand on his arm.

More time passed. The afternoon sun filtered through the branches and melted the snow. He began to doze from weakness. A pang of hunger shot through him like a light-ning bolt. He jerked awake. The top of the potato was just visible over the edge of the melting snow. Yankel eyed it hungrily. He needed it more than anything he'd ever needed in his life. The gendarmes, and the accompanying threat of execution, were the farthest thing from his mind. Nothing existed aside from the potato.

Yankel made to descend from the tree. He felt his brother's strong hand grasp his forearm. "Grab him," Zushe instructed. Hermann obeyed, wrapping Yankel in a tight embrace from behind. Yankel struggled, but to no avail. He was too weak to free himself.

"I need to eat," he groaned. His companions held tight.

The episode passed. He went limp, gasping on the bough of the tree. Zushe and Hermann retained their grip.

Night fell. The companions heard footsteps crunching in the partially-melted snow. He could discern the shape of a gendarme passing below them. The gendarme stooped periodically to collect the potatoes from the ground. Then he disappeared into the trees. Moments later, he could hear the sound of six pairs of boots departing the vicinity, punctuated by the occasional bark from one of the hounds.

They waited another hour before they descended from the beech tree. The gendarmes had left behind the remnants of a fire, but no food. Yankel hungrily chewed a handful of dirt. It was too late to return to Lucinetz without getting caught. They would have to wait until the following evening. They slept on the forest floor that night, too spent to reclimb the beech tree. Yankel dreamed of potatoes.

22

The lice and lack of hygiene in the ghetto began to take its toll. A typhus epidemic spread unchecked. Hundreds of the ghetto's Jews began to fall ill. The stricken developed hacking coughs, then fever, then a rapidly-spreading rash. Bodies piled up in the storehouse.

Doctors among the exiles did their best to help, but there was no medicine, no food, no hospital. The doctors began to contract the infection themselves. One by one, they lay down and died. Often, grief-stricken relatives took their own lives in despair. The smell of death intensified.

The work brigade activity ground to a halt. The Romanian overlords were too afraid to approach the disease-ridden inmates. They hung back in revulsion, shooting anyone who drew too near. The Jews were left alone to die. Yankel waited for his turn.

Zushe developed a cough. Panic bubbled in Yankel's chest. He patted Zushe's back. "You're fine, you're fine," he muttered repeatedly.

Zushe's cough worsened. The beginning of a rash was visible on his chest. Yankel scavenged the ghetto for scraps of food for his brother. He made repeated trips to the well.

The rash spread further. His brother's face became flushed. Yankel spent his days cooling Zushe's brow with a wet rag. Zushe's teeth began to chatter. Yankel began to pray.

His brother's eyes rolled wildly in his head and he muttered incoherently. Yankel heard sentence fragments and snatches of disjointed speech. He thought he heard Zushe talking with their parents, with Hirsch, with Uncle Berel and Mendel the baker.

Please don't die, Yankel thought.

His brother's flesh shriveled on his frame. His skin grew pale. He thrashed, moaned and passed into a deep sleep. Zushe remained in this state for two days. Yankel never left his brother's side. He dozed fitfully.

A deep premonition wrenched him from his sleep one afternoon. Alarmed, he looked over at his brother. Zushe was dead.

No one was there to help him bury his brother. He did it alone. When he had scooped the last layer of dirt onto Zushe's still form, Yankel rose to recite the *Kaddish*. He couldn't believe it. It never occurred to him that his brother would die before he did. Zushe was the strong one, the brave one. Not Yankel. It didn't make sense. It wasn't fair.

The ache in his gut was replaced by a profound emptiness. He was alone. He had watched as each member of his family was taken from him – little Hirsch, his mother, his father. Now Zushe, his older brother and erstwhile protector, had succumbed to disease. He knew it was only a matter of time before

death came for him too. He numbly realized that he no
longer cared.

23

The typhus epidemic ravaged the ghetto. Nearly half the occupants died. Their bodies piled up and were left to rot. No one had the strength nor will to bury them. The survivors of the epidemic wandered the freezing ghetto like ghosts. Many lacked clothing to cover their skeletal frames. They looked like walking corpses. Yankel knew he looked the same.

The storehouse was emptied by the guards one morning. The occupants were rounded up in the square, along with much of the rest of the ghetto. The inmates stood shivering in the chill. Dozens of gendarmes approached, whips in hand. They were wrapped in warm coats. The lead gendarme snapped his whip. "Move!" he ordered.

They began to march. They were not told where they were going or why. They were driven along at a fast clip, too fast for the old and those weakened by typhus. Thousands of Jews struggled to remain upright along rural and unpaved roads, thick with mud. Soldiers cracked their whips constantly. Stragglers were shot and left lying in the dirt.

They marched in this manner all day without break. Ukrainian peasants lined the road to watch. Some laughed and jeered. Occasionally, a peasant would approach a soldier and point to a Jew. The soldier would then pull the Jew out of the road, confiscate a ragged coat or whatever item caught the peasant's fancy, and hand it to him. The soldier then usually shot the victim.

Some peasants were kind. Groups of women took pity on the wretched captives and tried to slip them apples or potatoes when the guards weren't looking. They wept openly. Yankel wished he had the energy to thank them. He thought of the Ukrainian woman who had given him her dead son's shoes. He had walked barefoot through the snow to retrieve them from her after the incident with the potatoes. The march was brutal, and he was thankful for their protection.

Exhaustion wore on him, but he somehow managed to keep pace. Hermann was a different matter, since he had contracted typhus, and his condition was severely weakened. Hermann lagged. Yankel quietly urged him along. After half a day of walking, the lagging intensified. Hermann's face took on a grey pallor. He began to stumble. Yankel grasped his friend's arm to support him. They kept walking.

People dropped all around from exhaustion, pain, hunger, and cold. The grim procession left the road littered with the dead and the dying. The soldiers shot some stragglers and left others to be ravaged by the wild animals that came in the night. It began to rain.

Night fell. The soldiers ordered a halt and ordered everyone to camp. Yankel collapsed on the ground and caught as much rain in his mouth as he could. His feet were blistered, and he was weak from hunger. He did not know if he could rise again. He chewed on a few blades of grass. Even that small gesture took effort. He fell into a fitful slumber, freezing rain soaking him through.

They were kicked awake the next morning at dawn. Yankel painfully dragged himself to his feet. Hermann's eyes were open, but he seemed to lack the will to stand upright. His face had turned a deeper shade of grey. His spectacles were crusted with dirt. Yankel grabbed his friend's arms. With Yankel's help, Hermann stumbled to his feet. Hundreds did not wake up and remained on the side of the road where they had died in the night. The encampment stunk of human waste and rotting flesh. The march continued.

One woman lost her mind entirely when her child fell dead. She lifted the child and, babbling unintelligibly, walked in this manner for many miles. Eventually, she too was shot dead.

Hermann's feet were dragging. It was becoming increasingly difficult to support him. Yankel did his best to pull him along the rough ground. Their pace slowed and they began to fall back towards the rear of the procession. A soldier noticed.

He strode over and grabbed Hermann by the back of his shirt. The soldier hurled Hermann to the ground. Hermann looked up at the soldier, his face blank. The soldier shot him dead before Yankel had the time to protest. A pair of shattered spectacles fell to the mud. The body was left on the road where it lay.

They kept marching. Yankel said a silent *Kaddish* for his friend.

The march continued in this manner for another night and day. The road was strewn with the dead. His shoes, unable to sustain the abuse, began to fall apart. The heels soon began to flap with each step.

On the third night, the surviving members of the convoy reached a high stone wall. Situated on the Bug River, the wall was lined with three rows of barbed wire. There was a sign above the gate. "Death Camp," it read.

The ragged exiles were herded through the gate. Stone buildings dotted the enclosure. Yankel was driven with the rest of his group to an old barrack that lacked doors or windows. Planks lined the walls, leaving a narrow space in between for people to walk. A few Jews lay on the planks and stared at the newcomers listlessly. He had never seen such pitiful people, even in Lucinetz. Their skin was stretched across their skulls in a sick parody of humanity. They seemed barely alive. Their eyes betrayed a hint of insanity.

Yankel collapsed on one of the plank beds. His shoes were unsalvageable. Sixty percent of the people who had departed Lucinetz perished on the journey. He had reached the final circle of hell.

24

The Romanians needed roads for the war effort. To that end, Yankel was sent to work draining swamps. The prisoners, both men and women, were violently woken at sunrise and marched in a column outside the camp to the worksite. The men were handed shovels and set to dig. He dug all day, every day, shoveling peat and passing it up to the women who carted it away. The skin on his bare feet became translucent from constant exposure to the rancid swamp water. The skin started to break and pop. Walking became very painful.

The labor was grueling. He felt his enfeebled body wearing out. He concentrated on removing one shovelful of peat at a time. He dug his shovel into the swampy earth, lifted it up, dumped its contents into a pail, over and over and over. His shoulders ached, his arms screamed in agony, the shovel ripped through his calloused hands. He dared not stop. Rest meant instant death.

They were not fed in Pechora, as the camp was called. Not even the occasional crust of coarse bread or watery pea soup that he had received in Lucinetz. Pechora had one function: to kill. To feed the inmates was to defeat the purpose. If the prisoners were lucky, Ukrainian peasants who passed them on the road would let apples or onions fall to the ground. He risked execution by retrieving them, but death seemed more appealing than ever.

He survived mostly on leaves, bark, grass, and ditch-water. Several times, he witnessed inmates eating human waste. Once, he awoke in the night to find several people feeding on the corpse of a woman who died in her sleep. Yankel turned over and wished for death.

Starvation, disease, and execution were ever-present. Bodies littered the grounds of the camp. No one seemed to notice. Inmates regularly lost their sanity, running stark naked around the camp, raving incomprehensibly. Yankel almost envied them. Their minds were free of the torture that was his every waking moment.

Shortly after Yankel arrived, the entire camp prison population was herded, driven on by the prods and blows of the prison guards, to the center of the camp. A selection process began: the weakest were hauled roughly aside and shepherded into a huddling mass. Yankel, miraculously, was spared. At the completion of the process, the hundreds of selected Jews were crammed into the backs of several trucks.

The trucks departed the camp, their human cargo wailing in abject misery and fear. The trucks crossed the River Bug, where German *Einsatzgruppen* waited. The crack of rifle fire and the screams of the innocent carried clearly across the river and back to the camp. These *Aktions*, he learned, were performed periodically. Detachedly he wondered if he would survive the next one.

Yankel soon traded his ragged shirt for a bowl of potato peel soup. He lived and labored in nothing but a pair of torn and filthy pants. Months passed in this manner. He knew he would be near death if he didn't eat, but the camp was well-guarded and completely enclosed. The prison was enclosed on three sides by near-insurmountable stone walls adorned with razor-sharp barbed wire. The fourth side was open to the River Bug. He saw inmates hurl themselves into the raging waters in an attempt to swim around the wall and emerge on the other side. German soldiers stationed on the far side of the river liked to take pot shots at the swimming escapees. If the Germans missed, the prisoners usually drowned beneath the rapids.

He thought about his chances of slipping around the wall by way of the river. If he left early enough in the morning, the German soldiers might not see him well enough to properly aim their rifles. If he likewise escaped the notice of the Romanian guards on the Transnistria side of the river, all he needed to do was avoid being pulled under by the choppy rapids. Survival did not seem likely. He shrugged inwardly and decided to take his chances.

The next morning he rose before dawn and padded in his bare feet over the early-morning frost towards the river. He crouched low and kept to the shadows to avoid the sentries stationed in the watchtowers located where the wall met the riverbank. He reached the Bug and threw himself prone on the ground. He glanced at the watchtower. There was no movement. He saw a guard to his left at ground level. He dozed, his chair propped backwards against the wall. His cap was drawn over his eyes and his feet were crossed in front of him. His rifle lay on the ground beside him.

Yankel inched forward on his belly and eased into the

river. The frigid water walloped him. His breath caught in his chest. He feared he would pass out. He forced himself to start moving slowly through the water.

The current seized him almost immediately and began to drag him relentlessly along the shoreline. He fought to slow his pace, but his diminished strength was no match for the rapids. Yankel gasped for air and struggled to remain afloat. He began to pump his arms, determined to circumvent the prison wall and reach dry ground.

A strong hand closed around his left forearm and heaved. Yankel was hauled from the river and dragged roughly onto the bank. He was hurled to the ground, where he lay, coughing and shivering. He struggled to catch his breath.

He looked up; it was the soldier who had been dozing against the wall. He stood over him, arms crossed, a smug look on his face. He hadn't bothered to pick up his rifle from where it lay.

"You don't think I saw you sneaking to the river, Jew?" the soldier asked in Romanian. "I was hoping the Germans would shoot you, but no such luck." The soldier drew back a heavily booted foot and kicked him in the gut. Yankel curled up in pain, and once again fought for breath. The soldier kicked him a few more times.

"Get back to the barracks, Jew, or I'll kill you where you lie." The soldier spun on his heel and returned to his chair. He leaned back in his chair and drew his cap over his face, looking for all the world like he was dozing once again.

Yankel pulled himself shakily to his feet. He checked himself over. He was badly bruised, but miraculously, nothing appeared to be broken. Shivering, he dragged himself back to the barracks. Maybe he'd be able to catch a few minutes more sleep before he was marched to the swamp to drain peat.

He tried his luck with the River Bug a few days later. This time, he waited until evening fell, after the swamp labor gang had dragged their broken and tired bodies back to the camp. He crouched and slithered his way across the camp towards the river. With about seventy-five feet to go, he jumped to his feet and ran towards the water as fast as his wasted legs could carry him.

Yankel hadn't yet reached the water when he saw a pinprick of fire erupt in the darkness across the river. Something whizzed by his face. Belatedly, he heard the faint crack of a rifle. Without slowing, he hurled himself into the seething waters of the Bug.

He hit the water and submerged beneath the icy surface. Bullets cut through the water around him and embedded into the banks. Struggling to stay beneath the water and out of sight, he began to frantically swim towards freedom. His lungs burned from lack of oxygen. His arms were numb from the cold. He desperately fought his way through the water.

Something grasped his hair and pulled. His head was yanked above the water's surface. He was dragged roughly out of the river and onto the bank. He felt like his scalp was being ripped from his head. He gulped air into his lungs as he was once again hurled to the ground.

This time, the sentry did not content himself with a few kicks. Using his boots and rifle butt, he beat him mercilessly. By the time the sentry had tired himself out, Yankel was a crumpled, bloody mess.

He did not know how he had dragged his broken, barely conscious body back to the barracks. But he did, and he lay there for days as his body screamed in protest against his wounds. He alternately hacked up mucus and blood. His body shivered violently, rattling the other inmates crushed against him on the narrow wooden bunk. He drifted in and out of consciousness. He was so cold.

At one point, he sensed several men standing over him. One of them pressed something into his hand. They were muttering something. It sounded like a prayer. He thought he heard the words of the *Viduy*.

He relaxed and awaited death. He was ready. Death did not come. Eventually he felt his body emerge from its stupor and forced open his swollen eyes. A groan escaped from his lips of its own accord. His entire body was in agony. He felt a punishing hunger.

Dimly, he remembered one of the men who recited the *Viduy* pass him something. He painfully pulled his battered hand to eye level. It held a hard crust of bread. He ate it as quickly as his bruised face would allow. His shrunken stomach heaved from the effort, but he felt a tiny dose of strength return to his body. A wave of despair washed over him. He was still alive. Yankel closed his eyes and wept inwardly.

25

Yankel forced himself to return to the work gang before he was fully healed. Having failed to escape via the river, the only source of nourishment that wasn't grass and dirt was the occasional scrap spared by passing Ukrainian peasants. He limped along with the rest of the work gang, bruises checkering his bare, emaciated body, doing his best not to stumble and feel the wrath of a guard's club.

Sometimes he was lucky and received an onion or apple from a pitying Ukrainian, but more often he did not. The work was long and brutal. Every day, without fail, several workers slumped over and died from exertion, hunger, or a soldier's club. The bodies were left to lie in the muck. He often had to dig around the decaying bodies of fellow laborers who had been worked to death days or even weeks earlier.

He felt more enfeebled with each passing day. He sensed that, soon, it would be his turn to collapse onto his shovel and die in the mud. He was in constant pain. His bones ached, and his feet were blistered. His torso was covered in welts from insect bites and the blows of the guards. Hunger gnawed at his insides, waiting for the chance to seize the last vestiges of life from his emaciated body.

Yankel hauled a bucket of peat towards firmer ground one day in January 1943. His hunger pangs had reached a new level of intensity. He felt his strength draining with each herculean step. He feared he wouldn't survive the next *Aktion*. His head swam and he sensed he was on the verge of collapse.

A Ukrainian woman walked by carrying a basket of apples. She looked at him, her eyes blinking back tears. Glancing around surreptitiously, she tipped her basket. An apple fell to the ground and rolled to a halt at his feet.

He bent over and picked it up. It felt oddly heavy in his hand. He looked at the peasant woman gratefully. She risked the wrath of a soldier if she was seen feeding a prisoner. He felt his mouth move reflexively. "Thank you, ma'am," he croaked in Ukrainian.

"What did you say?"

Yankel jerked his head around.

A soldier was striding his way, his expression fierce.

The woman dropped her head and quickly slunk away.

The guard quickly drew level with Yankel and knocked the apple from his hand. "What did you say to that woman?" the soldier asked again.

He stammered. "I-I thanked her for the apple," he forced out. He eyed the soldier's weapon and wondered if the guard would shoot him or settle for beating him with the rifle butt. He guessed the former. Not that it mattered – He knew he wouldn't survive another beating anyway. He steeled himself and waited.

The soldier did neither. "You speak Ukrainian?" he asked.

He nodded, confused.

The soldier looked at him distastefully. "Come with me," he ordered. The soldier began to march away.

Yankel watched him go uncertainly.

The soldier looked back. "Keep up, Jew!" he barked.

They headed away from the swamp and along the dusty road, back in the direction of the camp. Yankel struggled to keep pace with the soldier's long strides. He thought regretfully of the apple back at the swamp. Another prisoner certainly would have gotten to it by now.

He was utterly confused. The soldier didn't seem to be interested in killing him. That is, unless the soldier had some cruel form of torture lying in wait. For a moment, he contemplated running into the woods and taking his chances in the forest. He quickly scrapped the idea. He wouldn't last long in his state. There was nothing for it but to continue along the road and see what awaited him.

They reached an administrative building about halfway back to the camp. The soldier approached and swung open the door. "In," he commanded.

Yankel was utterly bemused. He had no idea what to make of this sequence of events. He followed the soldier into the building.

The building opened into a room containing two desks and a number of filing cabinets. Two women, secretaries of some kind, tapped away busily at typewriters. An office was visible behind a glass-paned door on the far side of the room. Several soldiers milled around, carrying files and chatting. Everyone glanced curiously at him as he entered, and then returned to their tasks.

The soldier who had brought Yankel from the swamps turned to him. "Wait here," he said. The soldier approached the glass-paned office door and knocked. After several moments, the soldier entered, closing the door behind him.

He stood in the room, hands clasped in front of him, eyes downcast. He was painfully aware of his lack of clothes and his ribs jutting through his skin.

The soldier emerged from the office. "Come here," he ordered.

He nervously approached. He stopped in front of the office door.

"Inside," the soldier said. He did as he was told. The soldier closed the door behind Yankel. He could hear the soldier's heavy footsteps receding.

A mahogany desk, neatly organized, faced him from the far side of the office. A middle-aged man sat behind the desk. He wore a Romanian military uniform, and his hair was neatly parted. The man perused a document closely. He seemed not to notice Yankel's presence. He scribbled something on the document and studied it again. Finally, he looked up, his hands folded under his chin. He considered Yankel.

He knew he made for a wretched sight. He felt the man considering him: his ragged pants, his bare feet and torso, his emaciated and beaten frame. He could not read the man's expression.

The man spoke. "You speak Ukrainian?"

He nodded slowly. *Why did this man care?*

"How well do you speak it?"

Yankel cleared his throat. He was almost too nervous to form words. "I'm quite fluent, sir," he said.

The man nodded. He appeared pleased. "Can you drive an automobile?" he inquired.

Yankel shook his head. He had never so much as set foot in an automobile before. He sensed this might be the wrong answer. His stomach sank.

The military man waved his hand dismissively. "No matter," he said quietly, as if to himself. "That's easily remedied." He placed his hand back under his chin.

"My name is Colonel Loghin," the man said. "I am the new prefect of the Tulchin region."

Yankel stood there silently. That meant nothing to him.

The man continued. "The state controls a number of collective farms in the area." The colonel made a vague sweeping gesture for emphasis. "All the men are fighting for the Reds, so their property belongs to Romania now. My responsibility is to maintain an open line of communication with the women running the farms, make sure they are operating smoothly, making their payments on time, that sort of thing."

He remained silent. He still wasn't quite sure what this had to do with him. The colonel, seeming to read his thoughts, continued to speak. "I do not speak Ukrainian," he explained. "I need someone to drive me from farm to farm and translate for me." He fixed Yankel with a stern gaze. "Do you think you can do that?"

He felt a glimmer of hope. He nodded.

"Good!" the colonel said. He banged the desk in satisfaction. "Report here tomorrow morning at seven o'clock sharp." The colonel rose, strode to the door and opened it. "Ionescu!" he barked. One of the soldiers hurried over and snapped to attention. "Show him how to drive the car."

The soldier nodded his understanding.

Colonel Loghin glanced back over his shoulder and considered him once again. "First get this boy some food and a decent set of clothes."

He was led to a small kitchen area and ordered to sit on an overturned bucket in the corner. One of the secretaries brought him a tray containing a bowl of hot porridge, half a potato, and a cup of milk. His eyes widened. He had not seen such a luxurious meal in years. Not for the first time, Yankel fought back tears as he took his first bite. The secretary left the room as he consumed the food ravenously. He ate every morsel. When he'd finished, he felt both uncomfortably full and oddly energetic.

Next, the secretary brought him clothes. He was issued a shirt, a jacket, and, most precious of all, a pair of shoes. The garments were worn and hung off his skeletal frame but were otherwise in reasonable condition. Yankel blinked rapidly. He feared he was dreaming, and he would soon wake up starving and cold in his bunk back at the camp.

The soldier who had brought him to the colonel reappeared and ordered to follow him outside. A gleaming black automobile, open-topped, was parked out front. He caught sight of himself in the side-view mirrors. He was startled to find that the number of white hairs on his head equaled the brown.

The soldier motioned for him to climb into the driver's seat. Brusquely, he showed him the location of the accelerator, the clutch, and the brake pedals. He quickly explained how to properly gauge the tachometer and how to begin driving by shifting into first gear. Yankel noticed that, throughout the demonstration, the soldier failed to make eye contact and tilted his face slightly away, as if avoiding a foul odor.

His demonstration complete, the soldier had him operate the vehicle. Yankel gingerly drove back and forth a few times, the automobile lurching awkwardly. He cautiously eased the car along a few feet at a time; he knew that the Colonel's tolerance would disappear immediately should his car be damaged in any way. After a few minutes, he felt more comfortable behind the wheel and worked the shift with greater confidence. The soldier nodded his approval.

"Get back to the camp," he told him "Be here at seven o'clock sharp."

Yankel arrived a few minutes early the next morning. The automobile was where he had left it the previous day. He stood nervously at the vehicle's passenger door and waited for the Colonel to arrive. It was cold, as usual, but his thin jacket and shoes provided a warmth he thought he'd never feel again. He prayed that he would perform to the Colonel's satisfaction. He knew a return to the swamp was a death sentence.

The Colonel emerged from the administrative building at exactly seven o'clock, wrapped in a wool coat and wearing a fur hat. He was accompanied by an armed gendarme. Yankel opened the back door for the Colonel, who entered wordlessly without looking at him. He hurried to take his position in the driver's seat. The gendarme climbed into the passenger seat beside him. Slowly, he depressed the clutch and brake pedal. He eased the car into first gear, released the clutch, and moved his right foot to the gas pedal. He breathed more easily as the car rolled gently away from the administrative building and began to travel down the road.

The rest of the day was spent driving to various collective farms in the vicinity of the Tulchin district. The farms were small and dirty. Families resided in one-room cabins. Ruddy-faced Ukrainian farm women, heads and necks wrapped against the cold, spoke to Yankel about egg production, swine birth rates, grain yields. He listened carefully and then haltingly conveyed the information to Colonel Loghin. The Colonel would nod, occasionally asking Yankel a clarifying question or issuing an order. The conversation would continue in this manner until the Colonel was satisfied. The gendarme sat in silence throughout.

When they returned to the administrative building late in the afternoon, he was given another meal of porridge and milk. "Eat quickly and get back to the barracks," the gendarme ordered, breaking his silence. "Return tomorrow promptly at seven o'clock."

Yankel hurried to comply. He couldn't believe his good fortune.

Every day, except for Sunday and during inclement weather, he served as the Colonel's driver and translator. He still slept in the barracks, where his set of clothes attracted envious glances, but he no longer joined the march to the swamp to dig peat. With a daily meal to count on, he began to regain some of his strength. As the Colonel's driver, he was spared the threat of unprovoked execution. There was another *Aktion*, but he was passed over for selection as he knew he would be.

As the months passed, his driving skills grew more proficient and he transmitted information from the farm women with a bit more confidence. The Colonel was curt and unfriendly towards him, but he seemed satisfied with his driver's performance. More importantly, he never beat Yankel, nor did he order his bodyguard to do so. It was better than anything he could have hoped for.

Yankel began to entertain a dangerous thought. Is it possible that maybe, just maybe, he would survive this war after all? He dared not believe it.

27

The war was not going well for the Axis. Yankel began to hear snatches of conversation among the soldiers who sometimes milled outside the administrative building. Looks of concern often crossed their brows. He thought even the usually unflappable Colonel Loghin began to look slightly nervous. The Ukrainian farm women seemed almost haughty during the daily rounds to the collective farms.

The Germans weren't prepared for the Russian winter. They were struggling to fend off the massive Russian army. The *Wehrmacht* was growing desperate.

The sound of falling bombs was barely audible from the far side of the Bug. Occasionally, planes whirred overhead. Even in the darkness of the barracks, rumors circulated. No one knew what this meant. Could they ever hope to be liberated? The Romanians would kill them before that happened. Should they flee? Perhaps run deeper into Transnistria and hide in the woods.

Yankel sat in the corner as these discussions were held, saying nothing. He didn't know what to think. Each option seemed worse than the last. He would remain quiet and wait.

Escape attempts multiplied. Every day, more inmates were shot by Germans or drowned in the Bug. Those caught on the Romanian side were not spared. The guards grew increasingly anxious, and their cruelty grew to match.

One night, in early December 1943, he lay in his bunk and listened to the continued bombing. The Soviet forces seemed closer than ever. Yankel and the other prisoners could hear the occasional order yelled from the direction of the Germans across the Bug. The camp guards scurried about, more active than usual.

Dawn broke freezing as several guards stormed into the barracks, swinging their truncheons and dragging Jews from the wooden bunks. "Out! Out!" they roared. "Center of the camp, now!"

Yankel climbed from his bunk warily. A guard approached him. "Move, Jew!" the guard ordered. "Center of the camp with the others."

His heart hammered wildly. He gathered his courage to speak. "Sir, I am Colonel Loghin's driver," he said, barely above a whisper. "I need to report to the administrative building."

The guard looked at him, taking in his shoes and jacket. "Colonel Loghin fled in the night," he said. "You're no one special anymore." He shoved Yankel. "Now, move!"

He was hustled to the center of the camp with the rest of the prisoners. Thousands of Jews stood shivering in the Ukrainian chill. Yankel was grateful for his relatively insulative set of clothes.

Whips cracked, blows were meted out. Once again, he began to march. The procession exited the camp through the gates, under the sign that read, "Death Camp". They marched along the hard dirt road, past the administrative building, now abandoned. The front door swung on its hinges. The gleaming black automobile was gone.

They marched past the turnoff to the swamp and continued along the same road that he had traversed almost a year ago on his forced march from Lucinetz. They moved deeper into Transnistria, away from the Bug River and the war front. They marched all day. Sometimes they passed Ukrainian peasants. Gone were the cowed looks of a defeated population. They seemed to stand taller; Yankel thought he even heard the occasional jeer. The Romanian soldiers didn't react.

They were marched relentlessly. The dead fell all around. Stragglers were shot. Women begged for mercy. Men were beaten viciously. He looked at the ground and concentrated on putting one foot in front of the other. This was his third forced march, but he had a jacket and a pair of shoes. Yesterday, he had eaten a meal of porridge and an apple. He was determined to survive.

They camped that night at the side of the road and slept in the mud. The next day they continued their march. They were not fed. The familiar sensation of hunger began to gnaw at Yankel. More people collapsed. The prisoners begged guards for food but were roughly repulsed.

They camped on the side of the road again that night. Many hungrily chewed on dirt and grass. Yankel joined them. On the third day, he began to get his bearings. He knew the area. He had spent many days wandering these roads and woods with Zushe and Hermann, searching for food. He remembered hiding in the beech tree, the potatoes resting tantalizingly in the snow. Zushe saved his life that day, as he had on so many other days. Yankel's heart grew as heavy as his hunger was fierce.

They reached Lucinetz that night. The marchers, staggering from exhaustion, were driven like cattle through the barbed-wire fence. He saw the storehouse where he had lived for over a year. His father had died there. So had Zushe and Velvel.

The ghetto was crowded. He cast around for a familiar face. He didn't see any. Either the last year had scarred them beyond recognition, or they were dead. Yankel and several dozen of the surviving marchers were shoved inside a decrepit shed. He let himself fall to the cold ground. There was barely room to curl up in a ball. The hope he had felt during his time as Colonel Loghin's driver had all but evaporated. Death lurked once again. Yankel closed his eyes.

28

He was held in Lucinetz for another three months. They were not fed, and the ghetto was more closely guarded than it had been the last time he was imprisoned there. Slipping into the forest to beg from Ukrainians was out of the question. He resorted once again to eating what he could scavenge from the ground - dirt, leaves, worms. He soon traded his jacket for some moldy bread. His shoes followed. The little weight he had regained in Tulchin disappeared from his frame. His bones grew more prominent. Misery dogged him in every waking moment.

Occasionally, the prisoners were escorted out of the ghettos to work in labor gangs. They repaired roads, broke rocks, hauled debris. Mostly though, they were left in the ghetto to starve. Guards huddled together, whispering nervously. Occasionally, on the other side of the barbed wire, groups of soldiers could be seen running along the road, their rifles at the ready.

The Jews waited and, as they waited, they died. The cold and hunger carried them off, along with typhoid fever, infection, and murderous guards. His shed grew less crowded as time passed, as the living dwindled in number. Whenever he could summon the strength, he exerted himself and scratched out a shallow grave to cover their cold, thin bodies. Soon, the bodies grew too numerous to bury.

One afternoon, off in the distance, he thought he heard the faint blast of a shell hitting its mark. Then another, and another. The next day, he heard the explosions again. They sounded like they were drawing closer. The bombings seemed to increase in volume and quantity with each passing day. The prisoners whispered nervously among themselves. Wild rumors ran rampant. The guards were frantic. Yankel's nerves were stretched taut. He screwed his eyes shut and prayed for the war to end.

29

Romanian soldiers stormed through the ghetto, yelling and hitting Jews indiscriminately. The bombs were clearly audible. Planes roared overhead. Yankel could hear the report of gunfire in the distance.

A soldier approached his shed. He banged on the door frame with his rifle butt. "Get out! Now!" He banged his rifle butt again.

Yankel emerged, blinking, along with the surviving inhabitants of the shed. He caught the look on the soldier's face. He looked wild-eyed with fear. Yankel was seized with dread.

Throngs of soldiers drove the Jews of Lucinetz, pushing and shoving, through the camp and out the entrance gate. He was forced to move at a run, his bare feet snagging on rocks, his breath catching in his throat. They were brought to a halt at the edge of the woods. A wagon full of shovels was waiting for them.

A soldier unlatched the wagon, emptying the shovels onto the ground. "Dig!" he ordered.

Yankel grabbed a shovel and started digging along with the rest. His mind worked furiously. He glanced around, looking for an escape. They were surrounded by soldiers, each nervously fingering the trigger of a rifle. He was trapped. His heart was beating in an unceasing staccato against his gaunt ribcage.

It began to snow. They dug for some time. They were ordered to drop their shovels when the ditch was sufficiently long and wide. They complied. "Turn around!" the lead soldier bellowed.

Yankel stood, shoeless, at the edge of the Ukrainian woods, side-by-side with dozens of other Jews. Their backs were to the ditch. He shivered from cold and fear.

A regiment of soldiers faced them. "Ready!" their commander intoned. The soldiers raised their rifles. His mind went blank. His heart was beating so wildly, he thought he'd pass out. He heard wails, screams of fear, prayers, and cries for mercy.

"Aim!"

Yankel shut his eyes tightly. He thought of his home back in Czernowitz, the grocery store, his parents, his brothers. He began to mutter the *Shema*, the central prayer of the Jewish faith. *"Hear O Israel,"* he prayed, *"God is our Lord, God is One."*

"Fire!"

Yankel opened his eyes. He saw a burst of light and heard the crash of thunder. Something heavy slammed into his body. He felt himself falling. Then everything went black.

30

Meyer Leibovitch picked his way slowly through the abandoned ghetto, careful not to get in the way of the Russian soldiers. There were a few survivors, a few emaciated Jews who were lucky enough to escape the notice of the fleeing Romanians. Corpses were strewn all around – some in piles, others lying alone – their faces contorted in death masks, their limbs skewed grotesquely. He checked each body as he passed in case any had miraculously survived.

Meyer wiped tears from his cheeks even as he fought the feeling of revulsion that threatened to overwhelm him. He struggled under the equal weight of despair and guilt. Meyer had spent the war under false papers, hiding on a farm not five kilometers away, masquerading as a gentile. He had worked as a tailor for the Nazis and the Romanians upended his life, but he'd spent the last few years as a farm laborer, living in constant fear of discovery.

Meyer made his way through the ghetto gate. He walked towards the edge of the woods, where he could make out a shapeless heap covered by a dusting of snow. He approached, terrified of what he might find.

Meyer stopped in his tracks, his eyes wide with shock. Dozens of dead Jews, their corpses bloodied and riddled with bullets, lay in a mangled pile under the snow, their wasted limbs bent at unnatural angles. Their bodies, twisted from their death throes, tangled with one another in ghastly contortions.

Meyer fought the urge to vomit. He took a deep breath and began to gently kick the corpses. He made his way down the line, kicking each frame in turn. They were unresponsive, their eyes wide, faces frozen in their final scream. Meyer tried not to look as he continued kicking.

One of the bodies stirred. The movement was so weak, Meyer almost didn't notice. Meyer stopped, his heart hammering in his chest. He bent over. A man was tangled amongst the bodies, covered in a thin layer of snow. Meyer quickly wiped the snow from his face. He looked young, except for his hair, which was more white than not. Meyer kicked the body again.

The young man moved. Meyer started breathing erratically. Reaching down, he grabbed the young man by his arms and began to pull, disentangling him from the jumble of death. Meyer pulled the man onto the snowy ground and rolled him onto his back. He placed his ear to the man's mouth.

Meyer could faintly hear him breathing. Meyer jumped to his feet and began to run back to the ghetto. "Medic!" he yelled. "I need a medic!"

31

Yankel's vision swam in and out of focus. Where was he? Was this death? No, it couldn't be. His body was on fire. Death wasn't supposed to be this painful. Yankel saw a burst of light and fell back into oblivion.

He began to have visions. Were they dreams? Real life? He couldn't be sure. The pain clouded his senses. He thought he saw a man with a beard hovering over him, muttering a prayer. Was it his father? He concentrated. No, it was another Jew, a stranger. Yankel listened carefully. The man was reciting the *Viduy*, the deathbed prayer. Was that for him? He drifted out of consciousness.

An eternity later, he opened his eyes. His throat was terribly parched. The pain in his body had subsided to a dull ache. With an effort, he lifted his head and looked around. He was in a tented area lined with cots, each containing a wounded man. Nurses and soldiers walked between the cots, checking on the occupants and talking amongst themselves. He lay on one of the cots, his torso wrapped in bandages. He recognized the insignias on the soldiers' uniforms. They were Soviets.

The events of the last days of the Transnistrian imprisonment came flooding back: the ditch, the burst of light, the crash of thunder. He lay his head back down on the cot. He had survived. He couldn't believe it. He began to cry.

A young, bearded man came by the field hospital later that day. He smiled broadly when he saw that Yankel was awake and hurried over. Yankel thought he remembered that face from his dream, the one of the man saying *Viduy*.

The man introduced himself as Meyer Leibovitch. "You've been out for two weeks. I thought we'd lost you." So, it wasn't a dream. This was his third *Viduy* in the last year.

Meyer explained how he'd found him at the edge of the woods and pulled him from the pile of bodies. The story was unbelievable, even for Yankel. He felt at a loss for words. "Thank you, Meyer," he said simply.

Meyer smiled sadly. "I only wish I could have saved more."

Yankel recuperated in the field hospital for two months. Some of the cots were occupied by other Jews who had also managed to cling to life long enough to be liberated by the Russians. The hospital was grimy and dirty. Nurses were in the habit of hoarding bread and canned meat. Food was scarce, even in the army. Still, he was far better fed than he had been for the last few years. He had a cot to himself, and he wasn't in constant fear for his life. These conditions were vastly superior to what he had grown used to. Meyer came to visit often.

"You know, Yankel," Meyer said one day. "The war isn't over. The Russians are desperate for men. They're conscripting a lot of Jews from around here. They might even take you."

He gave Meyer a wry look. "You really think they'll take a weak, wounded Jew like me?"

Meyer shrugged. "They're taking almost anybody."

Yankel considered this. He'd heard soldiers talk about the fierce fighting at the front, about how there weren't enough guns to go around, how their officers sent them running into hails of machine gunfire without any consideration for their lives. He felt himself growing nervous. He'd survived so much already. He hoped the army wouldn't take him.

But take him, they did. A military doctor approached his bed one day as he was making his rounds. He looked Yankel over. "Stand," the doctor instructed. He did as he was ordered. The doctor observed his thin frame, conspicuous scars, feet marked by frostbite.

"Are you right-handed or left-handed?" the doctor asked.

"Right-handed," he replied.

"Lift your right hand," the doctor said. He did so. "Now curl your pointer finger." He did that as well. The doctor nodded and scribbled something on his notepad. He tore it off and handed it to him. "Report to the conscription station chief and give this to him," the doctor said. "You're now a soldier of the Soviet Army."

He gaped at the doctor. "Don't you need to give me a physical test?" he asked in shock.

"I just did," the doctor replied. "Your trigger finger works."

32

They sent him to Belarus.

Ever since the Americans joined the war in 1942, the two-front war had stretched the *Wehrmacht* to their limits. The Soviets, bolstered by their massive reserves of men and by American weapons, were steadily pushing the Germans westward. Hitler ordered his forces to take a stand at the northern section of the River Dnieper. The *Führer* was unwilling to yield another inch of his precious *Lebensraum*. The citizens of the Third Reich needed plenty of space to settle.

The Germans were stubborn fighters. They were filled with both a passionate loyalty to their homeland and a deathly fear of their dictator. The Germans dug in and returned Russian artillery barrages and machine-gun fire in kind. The Soviets, never a regime to value the life of the common soldier, hemorrhaged men to the German onslaught. The Soviet ranks were in sore need of reinforcement.

Thus Yankel, two months after he was shot into a ditch and liberated from the camps of Transnistria, found

himself on a train heading north. He wore the drab olive
green uniform of the Red Army. It hung loosely on his
thin frame. His head was protected by nothing more than
a cloth cap. He held tightly to his Mosin–Nagant rifle. It
was battered and rusty and had surely been wielded by
several now-deceased soldiers. He had never held a gun
before. The intricacies of its operation were still alien
to him.

He sat on a hard wooden bench along with dozens of
other new conscripts and stared out the window. The
Ukrainian and Belorussian landscape, in its full spring-
time lushness, was pockmarked with the scars of war.
Craters dotted the green hills. Entire fields were trans-
formed into black expanses of ash and dirt. Not a single
structure the train passed was left standing; houses, barns,
and entire villages were leveled in the fighting.

After two days of traveling, he arrived at the front.
Chaos reigned. Soldiers ran to and fro as officers bellowed
orders. Machine guns fired in unceasing eruptions. The
air was punctuated constantly by the sounds of mortars
landing and the screams of wounded men. Countless
planes droned overhead; Yankel could just make out
Soviet planes strafing German lines in the distance. The
terrain was jagged with barbed wire, trenches, and mines.
Tanks and trucks rolled through the mud. Bombed and
blackened vehicles dotted the battlefield. Two soldiers
hustled by, carrying a stretcher between them. The
stretcher bore a young man covered in blood, shrieking
horribly. Two bloody stumps protruded from his torso
where his legs used to be.

Yankel was sent to battle without any training. He was
set to work as a munitions runner. His job was to carry
heavy tins of ammunition from the supply line to the

fighters laying down machine gun fire on the front line. He darted back and forth, carrying two and even three tins of ammunition at a time, each weighing upwards of forty pounds. He kept his head down and ran, bullets kicking up the dirt around him, sweat pouring down his face, his arms burning from the strain, heart hammering, tins banging painfully against his shins. He knew to hit the ground face-first whenever the telltale *tchka tchka* sound of German sniper fire rang out.

Each hail of gunfire transported Yankel back to the edge of the ditch by the woods in Lucinetz. A rifle would crack, and a man would fall and with a jolt, Yankel was once again facing a line of Romanian soldiers, with rifles raised, the barrels staring him down. Fire and thunder once again erupted from the muzzle and he was falling into hellish blackness.

Men died in droves. As Yankel ran, transporting bullets to the Soviet soldiers, he struggled to keep his balance as he slipped on blood and tripped over dead bodies. The ground was littered with arms, legs, heads.

During one fierce day of fighting, he labored toward the front line along with another munitions runner, an Armenian lad named Hovik. Hovik was lithe and strong, and Yankel struggled to keep up. The shriek of the firing German *Panzerwherfer*, rocket launcher, pierced the air. The ground in front of Yankel exploded with a deafening boom as clods of earth were hurled through the air.

Hovik disappeared in a haze of red mist. Something wet slapped Yankel in the face as it flew by his head and landed at the base of a nearby sapling. He quickly glanced at the offending item. They were Hovik's entrails.

Yankel threw himself to the ground and covered his head with his arms. He couldn't shelter long; he needed to deliver the bullets to the front. The Soviet army leadership tolerated no failure from its ranks. Shirkers and insubordinates were assigned to penal battalions and deployed as human mine-clearers. These prisoners were stripped of their weapons, fortified with vodka and sent running across German minefields. Their mangled bodies marked the safe-passage corridor for the advancing Soviet troops. Yankel took a deep breath, drew himself to his feet, and continued running.

Sleep was scarce. He slept in snatches, no more than one or two hours at a time. There were no beds, no tents. The soldiers slept at the bottom of the muddy trenches as rats scurried by. Yankel's fitful dozing was often interrupted by a loud boom and the screams of the wounded as a German shell found its mark in a Soviet trench. The trenches were designed in a zig-zag pattern for this reason; the explosions were absorbed only by the section of the trench that was directly struck and the damage was contained.

There were other Jews fighting in the Soviet ranks. Some, like Yankel, were recently liberated from German-Romanian subjugation, surviving the killing fields of Transnistria only to die from the blast of a German Mauser. Others were local Jews who had hidden in the forests or joined partisan groups as the *Einsatzgruppen* slaughtered their families. Many were Russian Jews, often secular volunteers, who fought with a sense of national pride as full citizens of the growing Soviet empire. The Russian Jews, in particular, fought with a special ferocity. They were determined to refute the widespread impression that Jews did not fight as bravely or fiercely as their gentile counterparts. It was true that, on average, the Jewish soldiers were smaller and of slighter build. What they lacked in size, however, they made up in courage.

Regardless of background, no Jewish soldier advertised his heritage any more than necessary. Antisemitism was rampant in the Soviet war camp. One aged soldier named Ilya, recognizing Yankel as a fellow member of the faith, warned him to keep his religion as concealed as possible.

"In the heat of battle, they will shoot you in the back," Ilya told him. The old soldier was soon beaten near to death when a hulking soldier named Sergey, intoxicated from contraband vodka, sought out a Jew in the trench one evening and, spotting Ilya, set upon him with a shovel. Ilya's life was spared only when four other soldiers hauled Sergey off Ilya's limp and bloody form.

Rations were meager. The soldiers subsisted on porridge, raw onions, carrot tea, and vodka. Yankel skipped the vodka and took his meals alone. Most soldiers, and munition runners in particular, did not last long at the front. It did not do to make friends. He would find the driest spot in the trench he could, quickly eat his rations, and curl up to try to catch a few moments' rest.

Once again, his hopes for survival were low. His parents were gone, as were his brothers and his friends. He was fighting a brutal war on foreign land, surrounded by men who hated him, sleeping in the mud. He felt painfully alone.

33

The Red Army moved steadily westward as the outnumbered *Wehrmacht* reeled under the brutal Russian assault. By July of 1944, the Germans were pushed back as far as the western border of Belarus. Morale in the army camp was high as the massive Red Army crossed the border into Poland. Fighting remained fierce as Soviet soldiers were killed by the hundreds of thousands. Yankel, miraculously, continued to survive day after day. The bullets and mortars never seemed to find their mark.

By the end of the month, the Red Army reached the Polish city of Lublin, an important industrial and aviation center. The Soviet soldiers smashed through the German Panzer divisions and seized a network of important bridgeheads. The armies swept through the surrounding towns and villages, freeing them from German influence and establishing Soviet control in its place.

He was not with the troops that entered the town of Majdan Tatarski, but the returning soldiers, the Jewish ones in particular, appeared uncommonly grim. Word spread fast, and soon he learned of the horror they had encountered outside the little Lublin suburb.

The advancing forces had not been ordered to take the site but, espying the high walls and smokestacks, they figured it must be an enterprise of some importance – maybe military barracks or a factory of some kind. As they neared the wooden gates, they saw the barbed wire. The soldiers entered the enclosure. None present would ever forget what they found.

They discovered warehouses with rooms piled high with thousands of shoes – separated into piles of men's, women's, and children's. Another building, constructed of concrete, contained a room with numerous showerheads lining the ceiling. The only entry into the room was through a heavy steel door. Empty canisters were left lying in the vicinity. The canisters were labeled "Zyklon B".

The smokestacks were attached to a building containing a long row of ovens. Beside the ovens was a huge pile of ashes along with some human bones. The ovens were still warm.

The few hundred survivors revealed the true horror of the site. The returning soldiers described them as "the walking dead" – human skeletons dressed in rags, some walking, others crawling, their heads shaved, skin stretched across their faces. Realizing who the soldiers were, the prisoners sat in the dirt and cried tears of relief and pent-up pain.

The horrified soldiers soon learned that the facility was an extermination camp used to cleanse the Nazi empire of its Jews. The concrete shower rooms were gas chambers; the empty canisters contained a poison gas called Zyklon B. When the heavy steel doors were shut, the gas pumped in as the Jews clawed at the door and choked to death. Benches surrounded the gas chambers so that members of the Nazi *Schutzstaffel* guard corps could watch the dying Jews through small windows. The bodies were loaded into the ovens by other Jewish prisoners and burnt to ash.

The corpses were first dismembered so that four bodies could be incinerated at a time. The ovens operated continuously – twenty-four hours a day for several years. The ashes were mixed with soil and waste for use as fertilizer.

The soldiers found long pits outside the camp. The pits were full of skeletons, rotting corpses, and piles of skulls bleached to a deathly white. The pits were the remains of the victims who were exterminated by means other than gas – by firing squads, drowning in sewage, hanging, beating, and phenol injections.

Many of the battle-hardened soldiers broke down in tears as they related what they found. Yankel felt the familiar cold hand of dread clutch at his heart. He was transported in his mind, once again, to the killing fields of Transnistria.

34

Yankel was reassigned. He and a number of other under-trained soldiers were attached to a work gang and loaded onto a train. They were sent east, deep into the interior of the motherland. They traveled for three days. When they arrived at their destination, they alighted into blinding snow. Shivering, Yankel was led to an airstrip, handed a shovel, and told to get to work.

The factories in central and eastern Russia were operating at full capacity, churning out weapons, equipment, and supplies for the troops on the front lines. Huge cargo planes landed in the blizzard-like conditions around the clock. The planes were quickly loaded and refueled before they once again took to the skies to carry their shipment to the west. The heavy snow meant that the runway was perpetually covered with a layer of snow several feet deep, exacerbating the already poor landing conditions.

Yankel was one of a long line of laborers whose sole job was to clear the runway of snow so the pilots could successfully land their planes. He worked at this Sisyphean task for twenty, sometimes twenty-two hours a day. His cotton uniform was poor protection from the bitter Russian cold. Each day, he grew exhausted soon after his work began, but stopping to rest was not an option. As in the labor gangs in Transnistria, shirking duties could mean instant death.

The rest of the world disappeared, as his entire existence was narrowed to bone-deep cold and crippling exhaustion. The snow quickly seeped through his shoes, numbing his feet totally. His feet would return to life in a fire of agony for the few hours a night he was allowed to return to the barracks.

The man assigned to work next to him was a Jew named Avi Hecht, a fellow Romanian. He liked to talk to Yankel, tell him about his life in Romania, his experiences during the war. Mostly, Yankel was quiet, but sometimes he told Avi a little about his own life. He talked about the old grocery store and the *shtiebel* on *Judengasse,* about his work with Feivish the tailor, about the Soviet occupation of Czernowitz. Yankel never spoke about what happened on the far side of the Dniester. Some things just couldn't be put into words.

One day, Avi seemed to have a particularly difficult time shoveling snow. He eventually collapsed, bellowing in pain. He was carried off the runway on a stretcher, his face twisted in agony. Yankel kept shoveling. He later learned that Avi's foot had been amputated due to frostbite.

Day after day, month after month, Yankel shoveled snow from the airstrip. As time passed, the pace of plane traffic seemed to slow. One evening, the news made the rounds in the barracks. Hitler was dead. The Germans had surrendered in Berlin. Yankel kept on shoveling. He was still a soldier of the Red Army.

One day in early 1946, he was approached by an officer while laboring on the airstrip. The officer was bundled in a heavy wool coat and seemed none too pleased to be out in the open in such inclement weather. "Private Wiesenfeld-Reiner?" he inquired.

Wearily, Yankel came to attention and saluted. "Yes sir."

The officer handed him a sheet of paper. "You're free to go," he said. The officer turned on his heel and hurried away.

Yankel quickly scanned the document. They were his discharge papers. He was no longer a conscript of the Red Army. For the first time in years, he was free. His heart sank. He had nowhere to go.

35

Yankel blinked against the Italian sun as he disembarked from the train in Turin, Italy along with hundreds of other refugees. His thin frame was bronzed and hardened from months of travel, his cap faded from use. He carried nothing but a light rucksack on his back.

United Nations aid workers met the refugees at the station and led them to their new home, the displaced person camp in the town of Grugliasco, just outside Turin. The newcomers were instructed to line up in a single file, at the end of which they were served a bowl of soup, a slice of bread, and a cup of milk. He ate his rations hungrily.

The ragged group was then led to low-built barracks consisting of one long hallway lined with doors. The refugees were told to find lodging.

He stepped through one of the doors: it was packed with people. Men, women, and children, young and old, sat on small cots and on the floor. A couple of families had hung makeshift curtains in a futile attempt at privacy. The room smelled of clustered humanity. Noisy chatter filled the air.

He found an empty cot and slid his rucksack underneath. He sat down, his eyes alighting on an undersized pillow at the head of the bed, frayed and stained with age. He fingered it carefully. It had been years since he had a pillow of his own. His eyes filled with tears. He lay down, drew his cap over his eyes, and reflected on the events of the last few months.

After his discharge from the Red Army, he made his way slowly back home. It had been a harrowing journey. The war was over, but Jew-hatred remained prevalent in the local populations of Eastern Europe. Antisemitic gangs had taken to dragging Jewish passengers off trains and killing them.

As survivors trickled back to their pre-war homes, they were usually met with hostility by the residents of their hometowns, many of whom had occupied the houses of the deported Jews. Many Jews, having barely survived the Nazi extermination effort, were killed by their former neighbors filled with hate undiminished by the ravages of war. The Holocaust had ended, but much of Europe was still rife with danger.

He arrived in Czernowitz and found thousands of Jews living in abject poverty. He was aghast to learn that conditions had not much improved from the ghetto days. His family apartment had been claimed by a gentile family. He knew he had no legal recourse. He inquired about his brother Hirsch and his Uncle Berel, hoping against hope they were still alive, but information was scarce. There was nothing for him in Czernowitz. He decided to leave.

Yankel joined a group of Zionists who decided to make their way to Mandatory Palestine. The journey, he knew, was illegal and fraught with danger. Czernowitz was now a part of the Soviet Union and crossing the Iron Curtain was illegal. Even if they managed to cross the border, the group would still need to wend their way through western Europe, much of it unfriendly to the undocumented migrants and their cause. If they successfully made it to Italy, reaching the Levant would require illegal passage on a ship and the circumvention of the British blockade in the Mediterranean.

He was undaunted. He had surmounted worse odds. He was a *fusgeyer* now, a foot-traveler on the way to the Holy Land, just like the travelers he'd so admired as a boy in the Horeczaer Forest. He hitched up his rucksack and left Czernowitz, on the way to fulfill a lifelong dream. He never looked back.

The group of refugees crossed the border into the Old Kingdom of Romania in the dead of night. They traveled south into Romania's interior until they swung west and headed toward the Yugoslavian border. From there they changed course and traveled north into Hungary. Via Budapest, they passed on to Leipesdorf at the Austrian border, where they were provided rations by members of the British Army's Jewish Brigade, a group mostly comprised of Jewish settlers from Mandatory Palestine. These brave men and women made it their mission to ease the suffering of their Jewish brethren and help them start a new life in the Jewish homeland.

The refugees were transported across the border into Vienna in disguised trucks. Upon their arrival in Vienna, they received a medical examination at the Rothschild hospital. From Austria, they crossed the Alps into Italy through the Brenner Pass. Once in Italy, they made their way down the country's eastern coast to the displaced persons transit camp at Bari. From Bari, they boarded a train for Milan, where Yankel was subjected to an interview by a UN aid worker and was issued an identification card. From Milan, they were sent on to Turin until, three months after his release from the army, he arrived at the DP camp in Grugliasco.

The journey had been an arduous one. They traveled sometimes by train, sometimes on foot, moving in the dead of night to evade border guards and British troops. They moved easily in areas occupied by American soldiers. This was Yankel's first exposure to Americans; and despite the language barrier, he was struck by their friendly manner and willingness to help. The G.I.s were eager to point the travelers in the right direction and share their rations with the hungry refugees. He decided he liked Americans.

He also made a friend along the way, a young Polish Jew in his convoy named Yossel. Yossel was an extroverted and enterprising young man, with big dreams for the future. Yossel had evaded capture in the beginning of the war by hiding in the forest with a partisan group. They were later joined in the forest by another group of escapees who counted among them a young woman named Reichel. Reichel had executed a daring escape from the Novogrudok Ghetto and fled to the forest along with hundreds of other Jews. Yossel and Reichel became a couple. In Budapest, Yossel and Reichel were married along with twenty other couples in an improvised wedding.

Exhausted, Yankel closed his eyes and began to drift off to sleep. True, it was hot, crowded, and noisy in the room. But he had a cot, a pillow, and food in his belly. Soon he'd be on his way to the Holy Land. Grugliasco was paradise.

36

F ood in the displaced persons camp was not plentiful, and the long lines persisted. The rooms remained overcrowded and noisy. The lavatories were filthy and using them required waiting on yet another long line. As spring turned to summer and summer turned to autumn, the weather grew cold. Fires were not allowed in the barracks, so Yankel and his roommates used newspaper and twigs to build small fires that would not attract the attention of the campus police.

His sleep was restless. He often saw his family in his dreams: his mother lying in the mud by the tracks in Atachi, his father's starved frame in Lucinetz, Zushe's long, typhoid-ravaged body. He relived the cannibalism in Pechora, the cold depths of the River Bug, the vicious blows from the Romanian sentry. Most of all, he saw the muzzle of the rifle in the woods at the edge of the ditch as he once again fell backwards into oblivion.

He often jerked awake in a cold sweat to find that he was screaming. Too afraid to go back to sleep, he would clasp his knees to his chest and spend the remainder of the night sitting still, eyes wide against the dark. The other occupants of the barracks didn't mind these nocturnal disturbances – Yankel was far from the only refugee to scream in his sleep.

Work was hard to come by and many refugees resorted to drastic measures to earn some money. His friend Yossel was arrested for selling contraband tobacco and sent to jail. Reichel, at this point heavily pregnant, bribed a guard to have her husband released.

He was able to find work repairing bicycles at a shop in town. The bicycle shop was owned by a short, rotund Italian man named Angelo. With unusual kindness and patience, Angelo showed him the basics of bicycle repair and even began to teach the young refugee the rudiments of the Italian language. With his preternatural knack for languages, he was quickly speaking Italian almost as fluently as a native, albeit with a strong eastern European accent.

He found that he enjoyed bicycle repair work the way he'd enjoyed working with fabric in Feivish's tailor shop. Working with his hands, whether he was pumping tires, refastening chains, or tightening loose bolts, brought him a measure of calm from the nightmares that tormented him even in his waking hours. Concentrating at the task at hand and toiling for hours in Angelo's shop helped Yankel keep the dark memories at bay.

For the first time since the beginning of the war, he was able to resume his religious practice. Along with the other religious refugees, he observed *Shabbos* and the festivals. The local Jewish Joint Distribution Committee office procured a pair of *tefillin* for him. He once again began each day with his morning prayers. Even more than his work at Angelo's shop, the prayers and rituals brought him comfort.

He made two weekly pilgrimages. The first was to the UN official to inquire after any news about his brother, Hirsch. Week after week, he was disappointed. He knew that the chances that Hirsch had survived were slim, but he held on to hope that maybe his little brother had miraculously slipped through the Nazi web. As the months turned into a year, his hope faded away.

His second pilgrimage was to the local Hebrew Immigration Aid Society office. Each day he asked Esther, the young aid worker who ran the office, about the possibility of emigrating to Mandatory Palestine. Each day, he was denied.

"The British blockade is still in place," Esther told him. "Getting to Palestine is near impossible."

He knew Esther was right. Still, he returned every week to ask about the possibility of getting a visa to cross the Mediterranean to his homeland.

37

Y ankel's second year in Italy neared a close as he headed to the Jewish Joint Distribution Committee office for his weekly visit. As soon as he saw Esther's face he knew he'd be disappointed.

"I'm sorry, Yankel, still no visa to Palestine." Esther looked at him sadly.

Yankel's face fell. Even after almost two years, he still couldn't help feeling disheartened after each week's denial. He nodded and thanked Esther. He turned to leave when she called him back. "But there may be another option."

He faced Esther quizzically.

The young woman folded her hands on her desk. "We've located relatives in America," Esther told him. "They've agreed to sponsor you. The Browns, in New York."

He raised his eyebrows in surprise. He knew the Browns. They were distant cousins of his mother. Once, when he was young, they had brought their three small children to Czernowitz for a visit. He could not remember much about them other than that they seemed like nice people. But they were in America. His destiny was in *Eretz Yisrael,* the Land of Israel. He shook his head.

Esther sighed again. "Please think about it, Yankel. You've been here for two years. The visa to Palestine isn't coming. Go to America. Start a new life."

He considered her words. It was true that he'd grown restless in the cramped DP camp. Italy was just a stop in the journey, he knew. He'd been transient for the better part of the last decade. Maybe she was right. Perhaps it was time to set down roots in a new land. He remembered the American soldiers he'd met on the road to Italy. Americans were good people. And he had family waiting for him there, the only family he had left.

"All right," he told Esther. "I'll go to America."

He began the walk back to the barracks. It was time to start learning English.

38

He took a moment to marvel at the MS *Vulcania* on the dock in Naples. Her sheer size was breathtaking. The *Vulcania* was well over six hundred feet long and eighty feet wide. Her multi-storied hull was painted a deep blue, the superstructure a cool white. A giant funnel and two masts protruded from the deck.

He shook his head in wonderment. She was by far the largest and most beautiful vessel he'd ever seen. He took his place in the queue and climbed the gangplank.

He reached the ship's deck and looked back ashore. The dock was crowded with well-wishers waving handkerchiefs and hats, wishing their loved ones a safe passage. No one was there to see him off. A day earlier, he had thanked Esther and Angelo and shaken Yossel's hand before boarding the train to Naples, his Jewish Joint Distribution Committee-procured ticket clutched tightly in his hand. He hefted his rucksack and headed below decks to locate his cabin.

His cabin was in steerage, the cheapest berth of the

Vulcania's four classes. The cabin was small and window-less and contained two sinks and two sets of bunk beds barely wide enough for one person. A fluffy white pillow and a folded woolen blanket lay on each bunk. Above each sink hung a small mirror, two hand towels, and a bouquet of flowers. The room was scrubbed clean and smelled of disinfectant. Three other men, as shabbily dressed as him, were already settling into their berths.

He looked at his ticket in confusion, unsure if he was in the correct cabin. He had never stayed in accommodations so luxurious in his life. If steerage was this beautiful, Yankel couldn't imagine what the other three classes looked like. He hung his rucksack on a hook and climbed into one of the top bunks. He lay back on the softest pillow he'd ever felt, pulled his cap over his eyes, and waited for departure.

In time, he felt the ship engine roar to life. He heard the ship's horn blast and the funnel belch a black cloud of smoke. The roar of the crowd on the dock increased in volume as the *Vulcania* began to slowly push off from shore and advance into the Ligurian Sea.

His cabin mates headed above deck to take a final look at the Italian shore. Yankel stayed where he was. The European soil was soaked with the blood of six million Jews and millennia of inextricable hatred. Europe had taken his family, his friends, his youth, and his sense of peace. He would never look back.

39

Yankel watched as a green giantess, adorned in a crown and holding a torch aloft, rose above the horizon and grew ever closer. The immigrants of the *Vulcania* pressed against the rail surrounding the forecastle deck, straining for a first look at their new home. Many wept openly at the sight of the Statue of Liberty. He, too, felt a surge of emotion at the majestic statue and all that it represented, but his face betrayed nothing.

The *Vulcania* bypassed Liberty Island and anchored off another small island bearing a huge brick structure. The passengers crowded at the gangplank while ferries approached to transport the passengers ashore. He had to wait quite some time as the first, second, and tourist class passengers disembarked first. Finally, it was Yankel's turn.

He alighted on Ellis Island and was directed to enter the brick building. A veritable Tower of Babel awaited him as thousands of people packed a great hall echoing with dozens of languages. For five disorienting hours, he was herded into various lines and was poked, prodded, and questioned. Eventually, it was his turn to present himself to the mustachioed immigration official. "What's your name?" the official asked in American-accented Yiddish.

"Yankel Wiesenfeld-Reiner," came the reply.

The official scanned the passenger list on the *Vulcania's* manifest. "Jacob Wiesenfeld-Reiner" it read.

With a brisk stroke of his pen, the official inscribed a check next to his name. "Welcome to America," he said.

Yankel made his way down the stairs, bypassed the luggage collection depot and the rail ticket area and headed to the dock. A ferry transported him over the Hudson River and docked at the southernmost tip of Manhattan Island. He joined the rest of the passengers as they disembarked and stepped onto dry ground. He shaded his eyes against the sun and struggled to observe his new home through the throngs of passengers, greeters, and cab drivers waiting at the wharf. It was June 27, 1948. Yankel was twenty-five years old.

40

Sarah and Ephraim Brown and their five children waited on the dock in southern Manhattan, craning their necks to try and locate Yankel through the crowd. Sarah Brown had not seen him since the early 1930s when she and her family had visited Czernowitz. Yankel had been just a boy. After all the years that had passed, and all the suffering he had endured, Sarah hoped she would recognize him. He was Sarah's only surviving European relative. She was determined to give him a home.

Then she saw him. He made his way cautiously through the crowd, a worn rucksack on his back, a faded cap on his head. His face was young and unlined, but his hair was completely white. Sarah waved frantically at him. "Over here, Yankel!" she called out.

He looked over at Sarah. His dark eyes looked haunted, as if he had seen enough hardship to fill many lifetimes. He approached, unsmiling. Sarah embraced her cousin, tears streaming down her face. He didn't resist. He just stood there silently, not reacting as the Brown family bustled about, taking his rucksack and asking about his trip. Yankel barely said a word.

The Brown family took their guest on the subway back to their modest home in the Brownsville neighborhood of Brooklyn. The Browns tried unsuccessfully to coax information from him over dinner. Sarah noticed that Yankel's eyes widened when he saw the quantity of food on the table. Sarah brought him upstairs to show him his room. Yankel placed his rucksack on the floor and sat on his bed. He'd never had his own room before. He looked utterly lost.

The Browns did not sleep well that night. Tears streamed down Sarah's face as she listened to Yankel scream in his sleep.

At his parents' behest, Heshy, the eldest Brown child, took Yankel into the city to see the sights. Heshy was very small when he had visited the Wiesenfeld-Reiners in Czernowitz, but he remembered Yankel as a kind and gentle soul. Heshy was determined to show him a good time and help him acclimate to his new home. They went to see Times Square, the Empire State Building, and the murals at Grand Central Station. Heshy treated him to lunch at Carnegie Deli. Heshy struggled to maintain conversation; he talked about his family, the Brooklyn Jewish community, the plentiful job prospects for hard workers. Yankel didn't say a word, and Heshy eventually ran out of steam. They rode back to Brooklyn in silence.

Yankel screamed in his sleep again that night. Sarah and Ephraim sat with him in his room, whispering calming words and doing their best to soothe him. But there was no solace to be had.

He never smiled. He barely spoke or ate. He moved lethargically, his eyes hollow. His face constantly bore the same pained, questioning expression. "Why me?" it seemed to ask. "Why am I alive when everyone else has died?"

He was alone in a new land, and his despair threatened to overwhelm him.

41

The Hebrew Immigrant Aid Society, having learned about Yankel's experience repairing bicycles, found him a job in a toy factory in Brownsville. For six days, he worked silently and meticulously. On Friday, he informed his boss that he was a Sabbath observer and therefore could not report to work the next day. Yankel was promptly fired.

He was unskilled and in need of a job that allowed him to practice his faith. His options were limited. He thought back to his youth in Czernowitz, cutting and shaping fabric in Feivish's tailor shop. He remembered the peace it brought him. Yankel made a decision.

He borrowed three-hundred dollars from Sarah's eighteen-year-old son Alex and purchased a pushcart. He began to pay visits to the textile sweatshops that dotted Brooklyn and Manhattan. He bought scraps of fabric, cut the frayed edges, reshaped the cloth, and piled the renewed product in his cart. He then headed to Manhattan's Lower East Side, joining the droves of immigrant men peddling their goods on the streets of New York.

Selling rags on the street was a thankless job. Competition was fierce, sales were rare, and margins were low. He worked long hours and braved all weather on the streets of lower Manhattan. But compared to the labor camps of Transnistria and the airstrips of Russia, fourteen-hour days were nothing. Slowly, he developed a reputation as an honest man and a hard worker. He began to make a little money and quickly repaid Alex's loan. Only his relatives called him Yankel now; everyone else called him Jacob. He shortened his last name to simply "Wiesenfeld" – he found Americans lacked the patience for long, foreign-sounding names.

His business continued to grow. As time passed, he could afford to move out of the Brown home. He rented a room in an apartment in Brooklyn's Flatbush neighborhood. Eventually, he was able to buy an old station wagon. He began to drive to New Jersey, to the textile mills along the Passaic River, where he could get textile scraps even cheaper than he could in New York.

Yankel grew closer to Sarah and Ephraim Brown and their sons Heshy and Alex. He also got to know Sarah's sister Sylvia Stoffer and her husband George. He would often stop by for coffee and a chat in the Stoffers' Flatbush apartment. Still, he didn't smile.

As the years passed, Sarah continued looking after him, helping and supporting him in a thousand different ways. Yankel was touched by her compassion. Slowly, a little at a time, he began to open up to her about the horrors of Transnistria and the war in Europe. Sarah found herself unable to check her tears when listening to his tales.

He began to befriend some of the other young Holocaust survivors who struggled to find their way in New

York. Many of them attended the new immigrant trade schools organized by Rabbi Shlomo Halberstam, the spiritual leader of the *Bobover* sect of Hasidism. The Rebbe had lost his wife and two of his three children in the Holocaust. After the war, the Rebbe made his way to America, where he dedicated his new life to helping new immigrants rebuild theirs.

When the Rebbe's only surviving son, the saintly Naftulchik, got married, the young couple couldn't afford furniture for their new apartment. Yankel and his friends chipped in and bought the furniture themselves. After so many years of privation and depending on the largesse of strangers to survive, Yankel was gratified with his newfound ability, however meager, to provide for others.

He regularly took his meals at Dubrow's Cafeteria, a humming establishment at the corner of Utica Avenue and Eastern Parkway, popular with working class Jewish men. He was often joined by his friend Yossel, who by this time had emigrated to New York along with his wife Reichel. Yossel, who now went by Joe, struggled to support his wife and child as a carpenter. But he had big plans.

"I'm going to New Jersey," Joe told Yankel. "They're building homes there. There's a real need for carpenters."

Yankel shook his head at his friend's foolhardiness. "Don't go to New Jersey," Yankel said. "New Jersey is the wilderness. There's no way to make a living."

Joe was unconvinced. Yankel frowned inwardly. He would be sad to see his friend go.

42

The years passed and Yankel still didn't smile, but his business steadily grew. Eventually, he scraped together enough money to open a small textile store on Eldridge Street on the Lower East Side with his business partner, Alec Charitan. Alec was a pious Jew, a fellow survivor, who awoke every morning at four to recite the entire Book of Psalms before morning prayers.

Yankel's reputation for integrity spread, and fabric tradesmen sought him out to fulfill their textile orders. He met one such tradesman when he stopped by Sylvia and George Stoffer's Brooklyn apartment for coffee one Sunday morning. A man Yankel didn't know was sitting at the kitchen table and looked up as Yankel entered. The man wore dark-rimmed glasses and a smoking pipe rested in his left hand.

"Yankel, meet Gustav Van Dam," said George. "Gus is in the upholstery business."

Gus stood to shake Yankel's hand. He was tall and strongly built and appeared about fifteen years Yankel's senior. Gus' grasp was firm, his face set. Yankel liked him immediately.

Yankel began selling textiles to Gus and as their business relationship progressed, so did their friendship. Gus was a postwar immigrant from Holland, and his story was almost as remarkable as Yankel's. Gus' family was well-established in the Dutch Jewish community, and he lived a comfortable middle-class lifestyle with his wife, Miriam, and their two young children. When the war broke out, Gus was drafted into the Dutch army and sent to fight in the Pacific theater. There, he was captured by Japanese troops, tortured, and sent to work to death as a prisoner of war in the salt mines outside of Hiroshima.

Meanwhile, Miriam Van Dam took her two children, Jacques and Annie, and fled Holland ahead of the advancing *Wehrmacht,* leaving all their worldly possessions behind. Miriam and her children traveled to Indonesia, then a Dutch colony, hoping to find safe haven. Instead, Indonesia was seized by Japanese forces, and Miriam and her children were imprisoned in a Japanese internment camp. Neither Gus nor Miriam had any knowledge of each other's fate.

In 1945, the Americans dropped an atomic bomb on Hiroshima. As Gus was deep below ground in the salt mines, he was protected from the blast. After Allied troops freed Gus and Miriam from their respective captivity, they independently made their way to New York, where they reunited. Newly destitute, they settled in the Borough Park section of Brooklyn and set to work building an upholstery business from scratch.

Gus introduced Yankel to his daughter, Annie. Yankel was immediately taken with her. Annie was cheerful where Yankel was despondent, vivacious where he was reserved. With Gus's blessing, they began to date. Much to Yankel's shock, the heavy cloak of despair that was his constant burden slowly began to lift. He realized with a start that he now looked forward to the coming day when he awoke in the morning. For the first time since his boyhood in Czernowitz, Yankel began to experience a measure of happiness. He had almost forgotten what it felt like.

On summer Sundays, Yankel and Annie would take the youngest Brown kids, Moishe and Dassie, to Coney Island. Strolling along the boardwalk in the summer sun alongside Annie, buying ice cream cones for the kids, Yankel felt a million miles away from the barbed wire and swamps of the Ukraine. He stood on the sand and watched Annie laughingly splash in the surf with their young charges. He felt a sense of peace. Yankel smiled.

EPILOGUE

Yankel was reluctant to get married. He was too embittered by the war, too guilt-ridden at his own survival to move on with his life. But after much gentle coaxing from Sarah Brown and Sylvia Stoffer, he asked Annie to marry him. They were married in Beth Israel synagogue, Annie's family synagogue in Borough Park, in November 1955. Yankel had just turned thirty-two.

Yankel purchased a two-family home with his in-laws in Borough Park down the street from Beth Israel. He and Annie lived upstairs, while Gus and Miriam lived on the first floor. The four of them lived in that house and were members of Beth Israel for the rest of their lives.

Tragically, Yankel's suffering was not at an end. In 1962, Annie was diagnosed with a malignant brain tumor. She lingered for ten agonizing years before she passed. Yankel withdrew into himself, where he remained for the rest of his life. He never remarried.

Yankel and Annie had three children: Solomon, Emile, and Zipporah. As a young man, Solomon fulfilled his father's dream and permanently settled in Israel, where he married and raised thirteen children. Yankel's descendants now number twenty-six grandchildren and dozens of great-grandchildren. Many carry the names of his late wife, Annie (Chana in Hebrew), his father, Shloime, and his brothers, Zushe and Hirsch (including the author). And of course, many are named after Yankel himself. All of Yankel's descendants are practicing Jews.

Approximately three-hundred and sixty thousand Jews were imprisoned in the camps and ghettos of Transnistria. Only sixty thousand survived. The rest died of disease, starvation, exposure to the elements, and murder at the hands of Romanian and Ukrainian soldiers.

Ion Antonescu, the *Conducator* of Romania, was executed for war crimes after the defeat of the Axis powers. Colonel Loghin suffered the same fate after it was found that he arranged for thousands of Jews to be transported across the River Bug for execution by the *Einsatzgruppen.*

Yankel eventually tracked down Meyer Leibovitch, the man who pulled him out of the pile of corpses in Transnistria. He found Meyer living in abject poverty in Israel. Yankel supplied the funds for Meyer to start a small tailor business.

Avi Hecht survived the frostbite and amputation he endured shoveling snow for the Red Army. He too settled in Israel. He and Yankel remained lifelong friends.

Yankel's friend Yossel/Joe ignored Yankel's advice and moved to Elizabeth, New Jersey, where he established a multi-billion dollar real estate development business. Yossel's grandson, Jared Kushner, is the son-in-law and adviser to Donald Trump, the 45th President of the United States.

Yankel's textile business, while always modest, continued to grow. He traded his station wagon for a van and moved his store to the bottom floor of a four-story building on Broadway in Manhattan's Soho neighborhood. Yankel eventually bought the building.

He remained charitable for the rest of his life. He was particularly generous to the Beth Israel synagogue. The clock in the main sanctuary, a gift from Yankel, bears his late wife's name. Yankel was never late for services.

He was always a hard worker, rising early to work at his store six days a week. He never missed work until, late in life, he was physically unable to walk. His honesty in business became very apparent when he was audited by the IRS in the 1970s. At the culmination of the audit, the IRS wrote him a twenty-thousand dollar check.

Yankel died in Maimonides hospital in November of 2007. He was eighty-four years old. He screamed in his sleep until the end of his life.

ABOUT THE AUTHOR

Zvi Wiesenfeld studied Political Science at Yeshiva University and Forensic Accounting at John Jay College. He works as a financial investigator and business writer in New York.

He wrote this book to honor the memory of his grandfather, Holocaust survivor Jacob Wiesenfeld. He lives in New Jersey with his wife, Sara.

~

Dear Reader,

If you appreciated reading *The Man Across the River*, I'd love you to post a review on Amazon or Goodreads. Thank you very much in advance.

Zvi Wiesenfeld

ACKNOWLEDGMENTS

An astonishing amount of work went into writing this small book, and I am indebted to a number of individuals and institutions for their help in this endeavor.

First, thanks to the United Stated Holocaust Memorial Museum for the research they conducted on my behalf, without which the writing of this book would not have been possible. Thanks, too, to the YIVO institute, which served as an invaluable resource.

There are a number of works I regularly referenced. They are, in no particular order, *The Holocaust in Romania* by Radu Ioanid, *The History of the Holocaust in Romania* by Jean Ancel, *Here My Home Once Stood* by Moyshe Rekhtman, *Holocaust in Romania* by Matatias Carp, *Soviet Jews in World War II* by Harriet Muravand and Gennady Estraikh, Jewishgen.org, The William Breman Jewish Heritage Museum, The Ehpes Organization, The Azrieli Foundation, Yad Vashem, Bricha Legacy Association, The European Holocaust Research Infrastructure project, and many others.

Thank you to my publisher, Liesbeth Heenk of

Amsterdam Publishers, for believing in my manuscript and taking a chance on this book.

I would like to thank the friends and relatives who patiently allowed themselves to be interviewed, sometimes multiple times, about my grandfather and his life. My parents, Sima and Emile Wiesenfeld; my aunts and uncles, Miriam and Shlomo Wiesenfeld and Zipporah and Jonathan Ferziger. My siblings, Chanie and Chaim Yeshaya Katz, Ariella and Daniel Wiesenfeld, and Naomi Selevan, and my cousin, Baruch Ferziger. Thanks to the late Heshy Brown, may his memory be a blessing, and to Alex Brown and Dassie Nussbaum.

Thanks to Rabbi Pesach Korb of Beth Israel synagogue in Borough Park and to Avraham Glazer, one of a dwindling number of Holocaust survivors. May Mr. Glazer remain in good health for many years to come.

Thanks to my sisters Chanie Katz and Ofira Siff for their efforts editing my manuscript. Thanks as well to Mindy Kallus for her editing work.

A special thanks to my wife, Sara, for her constant patience and support in this effort. I would like to also thank Sara for the countless hours she spent editing and critiquing the book.

Finally, I would like to thank God for enabling me to complete this project.